BASIC DRAFTING

OTHER BOOKS IN SERIES

Basic Woodworking
Basic Electricity
Basic Metalwork

BASIC
DRAFTING

by

John L. Feirer
Head, Industrial Education Department
Western Michigan University
Kalamazoo, Michigan

and

John R. Lindbeck
Professor Industrial Education
Western Michigan University
Kalamazoo, Michigan

B

Chas. A. Bennett, Co., Inc.
Peoria, Illinois 61614

PREFACE

Basic Drafting was designed for use in a short, introductory drafting course. Its purpose is to help students learn how to make and use drawings. As part of a modern industrial education program, *Basic Drafting* includes the following as some of its major objectives:

- To make students aware of the importance of drawings in industry and to inform them of career opportunities in drafting.
- To teach students the proper use of drafting tools and supplies while they learn fundamental procedures such as reading a rule, making measurements, drawing straight and curved lines, and drawing to scale.
- To introduce students to the metric system and how to use it in making drawings.
- To help students learn to make simple shop and freehand sketches.
- To teach students the basics of lettering and dimensioning.
- To teach students the steps in making a working drawing, from selecting the principal views to lettering the dimensions and notes.
- To introduce students to the various types of pictorial drawings, such as perspective, isometric, and oblique.
- To teach students how to make and use sectional and auxiliary views with working drawings.
- To teach useful geometric constructions.
- To inform students about special phases of drawing, such as house planning, map drawing, and graph making.

This book is an attempt to make learning of drawing *simple rather than difficult,* and *easy to understand rather than baffling.* If a drawing course is successful, students will learn and will want to use the things they have learned about drawing. It is hoped that this book will aid in reaching this goal.

ACKNOWLEDGMENTS

Aline Lindbeck
Automobile Club of Michigan
Behr-Manning Corporation
California Redwood Association
C. F. Pease Company
CILCO
Eagle Pencil Company
Frederick Post Company
Harley-Davidson Motor Co.

Herkimer Tool and Model Works, Inc.
James Lindbeck
Keuffel & Esser Co.
Mayline Company, Inc.
NASA
North Central Airlines, Inc.
Schwinn Bicycle Company
UDM
Western Electric Corporation

TABLE OF CONTENTS

PREFACE 5

ACKNOWLEDGMENTS 6

UNIT 1. WHY STUDY DRAFTING? 9
Where Will You Use Drawing?, 12; Careers in Drawing, 12.

UNIT 2. DRAWING—A WAY TO COMMUNICATE 17
What's in a Drawing?, 18; What Are the Kinds of Drawings?, 20.

UNIT 3. READING A RULE AND MAKING MEASUREMENTS 22
How People Learned to Measure, 22; The Metric System, 22; Reading a Rule, 24; Tools and
Materials, 28; Drawing a Straight Line, 30; Measuring, 30.

UNIT 4. DRAWING VERTICAL AND HORIZONTAL LINES 32
Common Tools and Materials, 32; Getting Started on a Simple Drawing, 35.

UNIT 5. DRAWING INCLINED (SLANTED) LINES AND ANGLES 36
Triangles, 36; Kinds of Angles, 37; Drawing Angles, 37; Drawing Parallel Lines, 38; Drawing
Perpendicular Lines, 39; Protractor, 39.

UNIT 6. DRAWING CIRCLES, ARCS, AND IRREGULAR CURVES 42
Kinds of Compasses, 42; Locating the Center of Circles, 42; Adjusting the Compass, 43;
Drawing Circles, 43; Drawing Arcs, 43; Drawing Irregular Curves, 44.

UNIT 7. DRAWING TO SCALE 45
Making a Scale Drawing, 45; Other Scale Drawings, 47; Points to Remember, 47.

UNIT 8. DRAWING INSTRUMENTS & EQUIPMENT 48
Drawing Sets, 48; Compasses, 48; Architect's Scale, 50; Mechanical Engineer's Scale, 51;
Civil Engineer's Scale, 51; Metric Scales, 52; Drafter's Pencil Sharpener and Pointer, 53;
Templates, 54; Drafting Machine, 54.

UNIT 9. MAKING A SHOP SKETCH 55
Making a Shop Sketch, 55; Making an Isometric Shop Drawing, 56.

UNIT 10. DOING FREEHAND SKETCHING 58
Types of Lines, 58; Drawing Straight Lines, 58; Sketching Squares and Rectangles, 59;
Sketching Triangles, 61; Sketching Circles and Arcs, 61; Making a Freehand Sketch, 62;
Making Cabinet and Isometric Sketches, 63.

UNIT 11. MAKING A PERSPECTIVE SKETCH 67
A Simple Perspective Method, 67; Using Perspective Grid Papers or Templates, 68; Shading
Perspective Sketches, 69; Technical Illustrations, 69; Types of Technical Illustrations, 70.

UNIT 12. LEARNING TO LETTER 71
Kinds of Lettering, 71; Lettering Practice, 73; Lettering Devices, 77.

UNIT 13. DIMENSIONING A DRAWING 78
General Rules for Dimensioning, 78; Where and How to Dimension, 79; Drawing Arrowheads,
81; Dimensioning Circles, Arcs, and Angles, 82; Adding Notes to Drawings, 82; Dual
Dimensioning, 83.

UNIT 14. COMPLETING A ONE-VIEW (LAYOUT) DRAWING 86

UNIT 15. MAKING A WORKING DRAWING 89
Understanding Working Drawings, 89; Things to Remember About Working Drawings, 93;
Making a Three-View Drawing, 94.

CONTENTS

UNIT 16. DRAWING VIEWS WITH HIDDEN SURFACES **96**
Using Invisible or Hidden Lines, 96; Rules to Follow for Hidden, or Invisible Lines, 96.

UNIT 17. WORKING DRAWINGS WITH TWO VIEWS **98**
Points to Remember, 98.

UNIT 18. MAKING A PERSPECTIVE DRAWING **100**
Kinds of Perspectives, 100; Making a Parallel Perspective, 101; Making an Angular Perspective, 103.

UNIT 19. MAKING AN ISOMETRIC DRAWING **104**
Non-Isometric Lines, 105; Drawing Circles in Isometric, 106; Exploded Isometric, 106; Irregular Curves in Isometric, 108; Angles in Isometric, 108; Dimensioning in Isometric, 108.

UNIT 20. MAKING AN OBLIQUE OR CABINET DRAWING **109**
Kinds of Oblique, 109; Points to Remember, 110.

UNIT 21. DETAIL AND ASSEMBLY DRAWINGS **111**
Kinds of Assembly Drawings, 111; Detail Drawings, 112.

UNIT 22. MAKING A SECTIONAL VIEW **115**
Making a Full Section, 115; Other Sectional Views, 117; Symbols for Materials, 118; Points to Remember, 118; Conventional Breaks, 119.

UNIT 23. DRAWING AN AUXILIARY VIEW **119**
Kinds of Auxiliary Views, 120; Making an Auxiliary View, 121; Points to Remember, 122.

UNIT 24. DOING USEFUL GEOMETRIC CONSTRUCTION **123**

UNIT 25. ARCHITECTURAL DRAWINGS **129**
Making a Room Arrangement or Lab Layout, 130; Planning an Addition, 130; Kinds of Construction, 132; Drawings for a Home, 134.

UNIT 26. MAP DRAWINGS **146**
Common Kinds of Maps, 146.

UNIT 27. GRAPHS AND CHARTS **152**
Line and Curve Graph, 153; Bar Graph, 154; Circle, Pie, or Sector Graphs, 155; Pictorial Graph, 155; Charts, 155.

UNIT 28. HOW PRINTS ARE MADE **157**
How Prints Are Made, 157; Blueprint Machine, 158; Ozalid Process (Dry Diazo), 158; Bruning Copyflex Process (Moist Diazo), 160; Microfilming, 160; Other Duplicating Processes, 160.

QUESTIONS AND TOPICS FOR DISCUSSION **161**

INDEX **165**

Unit 1. Why Study Drafting?

This is the age of marvels—atomic power, jet airplanes, space travel, and electronic devices that work wonders. To live better and enjoy life more in this wonderful age, you will need to know how to make and read drawings. Why? Here are only a few of many reasons:

1. To Read Well. You can't pick up a book or magazine today without seeing a drawing of some kind. A science book has many drawings that show how things work. Fig. 1-1. Any popular magazine may have drawings of new products. Some mathematics books contain drawings of many kinds of *geometric* shapes. A geography book is full of maps.

2. To Understand How Things Operate and How to Use Them. When you buy an unassembled, boxed product you find an instruction sheet with it. It usually contains a drawing to tell you how to put the product together, take care of it, repair it, or order a new part for it. Mechanical or electrical things can be explained best by drawings. Fig. 1-2 (P. 10).

3. To Plan Wisely and Well. People who want to build a home or vacation cabin must first be able to read the plans to find out if they suit their needs. Figs. 1-3 and 1-4. In order to take a trip you must be able to read a road map drawing. In many games, such as football, you must be able to read diagrams or drawings of the plays. This helps you to plan your play and to play wisely.

4. To Build or Make Things. Everything that is built must first be drawn. In the workshop you need a drawing or sketch of each project you are going to build. In woodwork it might be a spice rack, or in metal-

1-1. *A simple telephone circuit. The speaker's voice sets up sound waves in the air. The sound waves are converted into electrical impulses, sent over the wire, and changed again into sound waves for the ear at the other end.*

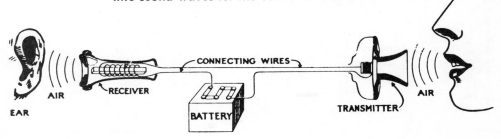

work, a bow and arrow rack. If you are able to make a good sketch or drawing, the job is well started.

In American industry, everything that is made, manufactured, or built must first be put on paper as a drawing. When a new automobile or airplane is to be built, thousands of drawings of all kinds must be made. Everyone who helps to build it must

1-2. *An exploded assembly drawing naming the important parts of the brakes for a bicycle.*

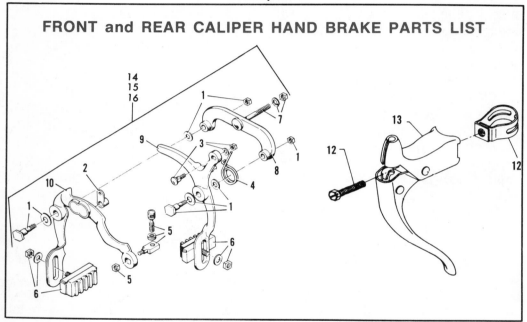

FRONT and REAR CALIPER HAND BRAKE PARTS LIST

KEY NO.	PART NO.	DESCRIPTION	LIST PRICE	KEY NO.	PART NO.	DESCRIPTION	LIST PRICE
1	304549	Bearing Screw, w/Nuts and Washers	.35		304557	Right Brake Arm (SIII Stamped on Arm)	1.57
2	304550	Nylon Roller	.20	10	304553	Left Brake Arm (SII Stamped on Arm)	1.34
3	304500	Cable Anchor Bolt w/Nut and Washer	.33		304558	Left Brake Arm (SIII Stamped on Arm)	1.57
4	304551	Brake Spring	.33				
5	304503	Adjusting Barrel Assembly	.31	11	308698	Brake Cable. Casing and Ferrule	1.23
6	308697	Brake Shoe w/Nut and Washer	.26	12	304556	Lever Handbrake Clamp w/Attaching Hdwe.	1.16
7	304560	Front Spindle Bolt w/Nut and Washer	.58	13	304555	Lever Handbrake Complete- Less Cable	2.89
	304561	Rear Spindle Bolt	.46	14	304570	Front Caliper Brake Stirrup Assy.	3.29
8	304554	Horseshoe (10/70 Stamped on Shoe)	.77	15	304573	Rear Caliper Brake - Stirrup Assy. Boys Only	3.47
	304559	Horseshoe (18/73 Stamped on Shoe)	.84	16	304572	Rear Caliper Brakes - Stirrup Assy. Girls Only	3.47
9	304552	Right Brake Arm (SII Stamped on Arm)	1.34				

1-3. *A rendering, or pictorial drawing, of a simple cabin.*

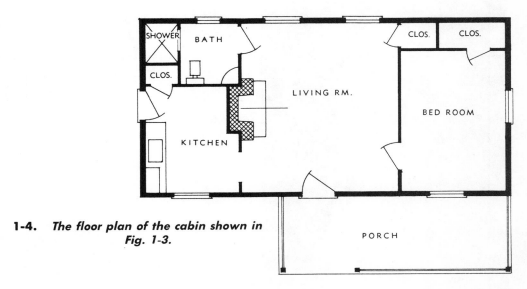

1-4. *The floor plan of the cabin shown in Fig. 1-3.*

PARALLEL BURN

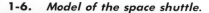

HO TANK
(29 FT DIA × 150 FT LONG)

13 FT

167 FT

120 FT

130 FT

75 FT

80 FT

1-5. *Simplified drawing of a space shuttle.*

1-6. *Model of the space shuttle.*

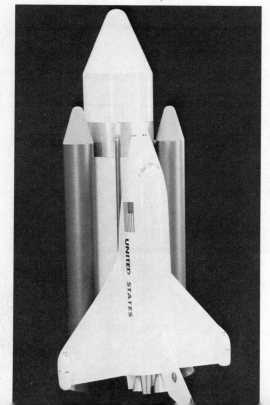

UNITED STATES

know either how to make or read these drawings. The designer, engineer, and drafter must know how to carry out the idea. They also make sketches, check them, and make the finished drawings. Figs. 1-5 and 1-6. The people who purchase supplies and materials need to be able to read drawings. The skilled workers responsible for making the product would be lost without drawings. Drawings are the master plans that everyone follows.

WHERE WILL YOU USE DRAWINGS?

The most important reason for learning drawing now is to use this knowledge in the laboratory. It doesn't make any difference what materials you are going to use. First you learn to make the drawing from which the project is to be built. You will also use these drawing skills in other school activities—in science, mathematics, geography, and social science. Many of the drawings will be useful in your hobbies, in sports, and in the things you do around your home. You will find that this book contains drawings representing all kinds of activities. Remember that drawing is *visual communication*, a way of telling and showing by using pictures instead of words or real objects. You can tell more and understand better with drawings.

CAREERS IN DRAWING

Well over three-quarters of a million men and women have jobs in which they must know how to draw and design. Millions of others have to know how to use and to read drawings. Fig. 1-7. Remember, almost everything that is made or built must first be drawn. There are many opportunities in drafting and design. Some of these are described in the following paragraphs.

Training, practice, patience, and attention to detail are important in developing drafting skills. Through the years, various grades of drafting ability have been defined to tell the learner from the more experienced person. Here are some of the drafting jobs:

Learner or Junior Detailer. This is a beginner, with little or no drafting experience, who has the ability and willingness to learn. The junior detailer must know how to do simple detail and assembly drawings. Precise work in drafting is important. After becoming skilled at making detail and assembly drawings, and doing copying and tracing work accurately, he or she can be promoted to the next level.

Detailer. The detailer draws more difficult detail and assembly drawings and makes changes in these drawings. The detailer usually works from sketches, other drawings, outlines, or notes. A greater skill is need-

1-7.   *People in the military service, such as these Coast Guard men, must possess skills in making and reading map drawings.*   13

1-8. *A skilled drafter at work.*

ed for the more complex drawings. Fig. 1-8.

Senior Detailer. The senior detailer must be able to make design drawings. He or she draws detail, assembly, and installation drawings exactly to scale, which may be a very complex task involving many problems.

The Junior Designer. This person works from notes and specifications. While there is some similarity between the work of the junior designer and senior detailer, the junior designer is involved in more actual design work. Guided by an experienced drafter and designer, he or she learns how to make design layouts from engineering sketches.

Layout Drafter. The layout drafter prepares drawings from specifications, from written descriptions of details not shown on drawings, and from sketches and notes furnished by the engineer and scientist. The layout drafter must understand manufacturing machines and production methods.

Designer. This is the major goal of many drafters. On the designer's board, creative ideas come to life. The designer works closely with technicians, engineers, and scientists whose knowledge of machines and operating principles of mechanics helps determine the details of any design. Graphics designers specialize in layouts for advertising, packaging, and related graphic arts activities. Fig. 1-9.

Technical Illustrator. The technical illustrator makes pictorial drawings or retouches photographs to show products in different stages of development. The illustrations are for showing a new product, for use during manufacturing, and for repair manuals. The technical illustrator must have a combination of technical and artistic training. Artistic ability is especially important in making realistic drawings of things yet to be built. Since almost all technical illustrations have some type of freehand or machine lettering, the technical illustrator must be trained to use brushes and markers, as well as mechanical drawing equipment.

There are at least two good ways of becoming a drafter: (1) You can begin by taking all of the drafting courses possible in high school. Then you can go to a trade, vocational, or technical school and take a one- to two-year program in this trade. In these schools, in addition to drafting, you will study math, science, English, and common manufacturing processes. (2) A second way is to serve a three- or four-year apprenticeship in the trade. Here you sign a contract to work with experienced drafters until you have learned the trade.

In drafting, wages and salaries are somewhat lower than in other trades during the early years. However, with experience and training come many opportunities. Most drafters specialize in some area of work such as architectural, structural, mechanical, aeronautical, electrical, marine, or map drafting. They usually work for private drafting companies, manufacturers, or for the government.

Tool Designers. The tool designer works from the drawings made by the industrial designer and engineer. The first step is to make sketches of the design for the tools, dies, jigs, and fixtures that are needed to make the parts of a product. These sketches are made into working drawings and checked to see if they are correct and will work. The drawings are then given to the tool and die makers who build the tools and fixtures. The tool designer must have a good understanding of designing processes, including machines and drawing, and must know all about materials and how they can be worked. Most tool designers start as drafters or machinists. They receive additional training and eventually become experts in their field. Many former industrial arts teachers become tool designers be-

1-9. *This graphic designer is completing layouts for a packaging problem.*

cause of their general knowledge of drawing and machine shop.

If you plan to get a college degree, there are many other occupations open to you in drawing and design.

Architects. This occupation offers wonderful opportunities for anyone who is creative. The architect designs all kinds of new homes and buildings. Most architects specialize in home designing or commercial, industrial, or public structures. There are about 40,000 architects in the United States.

A degree in architecture requires four to five years of study. Then most architects spend a year or two working for a large firm, getting practical experience. Most states require that architects be licensed, especially when the health and welfare of people are the concern of these architects. After getting their license, most architects become self-employed.

Before designing a new building or home, the architect calls on the people concerned to discuss such things as location, size, cost, and materials. Next, preliminary sketches are made, including a pictorial drawing or rendering of the proposed building. After these are checked and okayed by the client, the architect and the drafters prepare detailed drawings of the structure to be used by the contractor or builder. Often the architect will also arrange for a contractor and will help to supervise the construction.

Industrial Designer. These are the people who design the new car models, refrigerators, and other things we buy and use. The industrial designer usually works for a large company or for an independent concern that does designing. Usually the designs are made in the form of pictorial drawings or models. Industrial designers must be artistic and creative and be able to draw. They work closely with engineers in deciding if the product can be built. Designers usually specialize in some area such as automotive, electrical, or furniture design. The industrial designer must have a good background in art, manufacturing processes, mathematics and other areas dealing with business and industry. Some industrial designers transfer from drafting, commercial art, or teaching. Many, however, are trained in college as industrial designers.

Teachers. If you like drawing and shop work you will find many opportunities in teaching. There are about 150,000 industrial arts teachers who teach drawing either as a part-time or full-time activity. Some teach in general shops while others teach full-time drawing. If you like to work with other people, if you like the freedom teaching gives, and if you want to be of service to others, you should consider teaching. Fig. 1-10.

Engineers. There are over one million engineers in the United States, and this number is growing rapidly. Engineers design, build, test, and operate the things we use and live with. They usually specialize in one field, such as mechanical, electrical, chemical or civil engineering. Every

1-10. *Teaching drawing to young people is a challenging and rewarding career.*

engineer must learn basic drawing and also the engineering drawing necessary to his or her specialty. There is a tremendous need for more engineers. If you are good at math, the sciences, and drawing, you should consider an engineering career.

Self-Test. Can you be a drafter, teacher, designer, or engineer? Here is a simple test to help you find out if you're interested in becoming a drafter or would like to become a member of one of the professions described in this unit.

1. Do you like mechanical things?

2. Do you like to build things such as models?

3. Is your work neat and accurate?

4. Can you stay with a job until it is completed?

5. Are you pretty good in math and science?

6. Can you see something on paper and imagine how it really looks?

If your answer is "yes" to all of these questions, then you might consider an occupation in which drawing and designing are important.

Unit 2. Drawing — A Way to Communicate

Drawing is a way of telling and showing by using pictures instead of words or real objects. This is called *visual communication*, a way of describing something through pictures which you can see and study. In this kind of communication certain symbols are used which help to give information or directions quickly. Look at the traffic signs in Fig. 2-1. When you are driving a bicycle or an automobile, you don't have time to read a lot of words on a traffic sign, but you can understand symbols immediately.

2-1. *New traffic signs (on the right) use fewer words and more symbols.*

Have you ever tried to explain or describe some new gadget to a friend? Often you will say, "Just a minute and I'll show you!" You get a piece of paper and a pencil and make a sketch of the object. You are *drawing*. A famous designer of cars has said, "Drawing is what you put on paper after you have done a lot of thinking." That's true because it's a way of getting ideas across to some-one else.

Drawings are of two kinds. *Illustrative* drawings show *how a thing looks* and *construction* drawings tell *how to make that thing.* Sometimes one drawing can do both of these jobs. In this course you will be interested most of all in drawings that tell how to make something.

WHAT'S IN A DRAWING?

You have used drawings many times. A road map is a kind of drawing. You may have built a craft project and used a drawing to help you. Drawing is not new to you or hard to learn. There are, however, many *things* to learn. New ideas and ways of working will come easy and one at a time as you use this book and work with your instructor and other students.

There are three basic things that go to make up all drawings. These are: (1) *lines*, (2) *dimensions* or *sizes*, and (3) *symbols*. The shape of an object is shown with *lines*. These lines are vertical (up and down), horizontal (right and left), slanted or inclined, and curved or circular (round). Fig. 2-2 shows the vertical, horizontal, and slanted lines found in a fishing tackle box such as the one in Fig. 2-3. Curved or circular lines show the shape of such things as the sides of a fruit dish, Fig. 2-4, or a baseball, Fig. 2-5. Lines also tell other things by the way they are drawn. You will see this later.

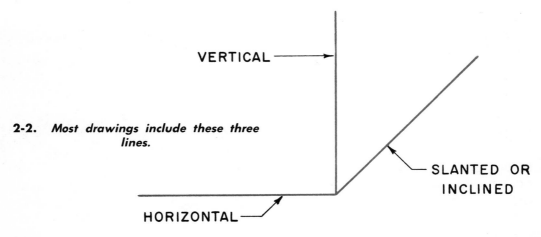

2-2. *Most drawings include these three lines.*

VERTICAL

SLANTED OR INCLINED

HORIZONTAL

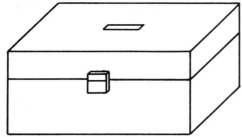

2-3. *Vertical, horizontal, and inclined lines make up the shape of this fishing tackle box.*

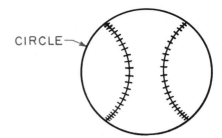

2-5. *A circle shows the shape of this baseball.*

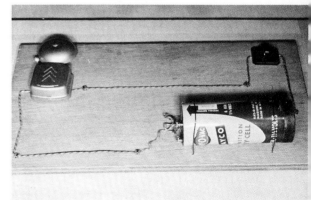

2-4. *A curve shows the shape of this candy dish.*

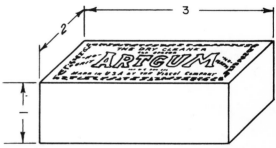

2-6. *The numbers give the size (dimensions) of the eraser.*

Dimensions tell what size a thing is. Dimensions are the numbers you see on a drawing. Without these it would be impossible to build or make things correctly. Fig. 2-6.

The third basic part in drawing is the *symbol.* A symbol is a very simple drawing of an object. Most things are too difficult or take too much time to draw exactly as they are. Therefore, symbols are used instead. In Fig. 2-1 you saw some examples of how symbols are used. Another example is shown here. Fig. 2-7 is a photograph of a bell, a push button, and a battery. In Fig. 2-8 (P. 20) these same objects are shown in symbols. In each area of drawing there is a different group of symbols to use.

2-7. *Photograph of the parts of a simple bell circuit.*

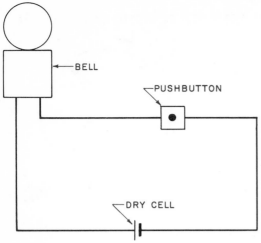

2-8. *A drawing of a bell circuit using symbols. This is called a schematic diagram or drawing.*

2-9. *A photograph of a print machine.*

WHAT ARE THE KINDS OF DRAWINGS?

Figs. 2-9 to 2-13 are a photograph of a print machine and four different kinds of drawings of it. Notice that three of these look a good deal like the photograph. Fig. 2-9. These are called *pictorial drawings*. The one that is most like the photograph, Fig. 2-10, is called a *perspective* drawing. The other two pictorial drawings are called *cabinet* (Fig. 2-11) and *isometric* (Fig. 2-12). The fourth drawing (Fig. 2-13) looks the least like the photograph, but it is the most useful. It is often called a *working drawing*, since it is used so often by workers and builders. Some call it a *multiview* (many view) drawing, since it usually shows two or three views of the object. Still another term is *orthographic projection*. Let's call it a *working drawing!*

2-10. *A perspective drawing of the print machine.*

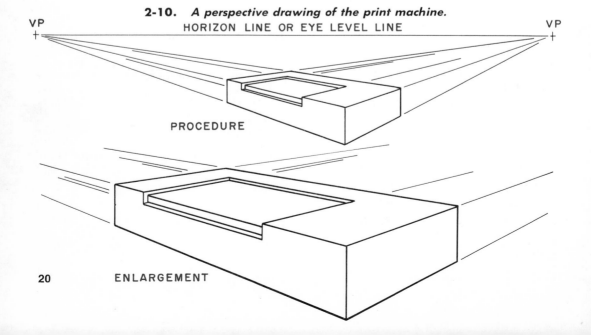

HORIZON LINE OR EYE LEVEL LINE

VP

VP

PROCEDURE

ENLARGEMENT

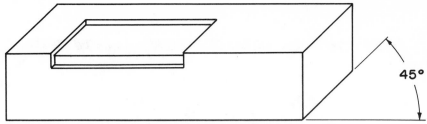

2-11. *A cabinet drawing of the print machine.*

45°

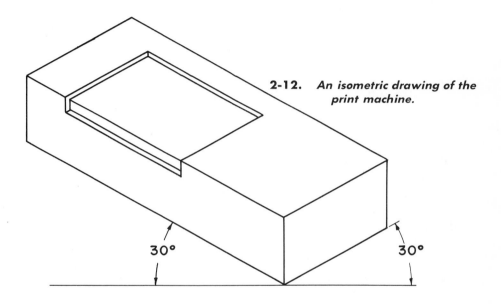

2-12. *An isometric drawing of the print machine.*

30°   30°

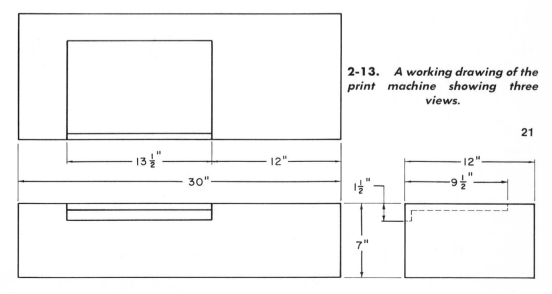

2-13. *A working drawing of the print machine showing three views.*

$13\frac{1}{2}$"   12"

30"

$1\frac{1}{2}$"   12"

$9\frac{1}{2}$"

7"

Unit 3. Reading a Rule and Making Measurements

How tall are you? Are you 5'6" or 1.35 metres or taller or shorter than the student next to you? Your exact height can be found only by measuring, and there are different kinds of measuring systems. The two most widely used are the customary (inch) and the metric system.

In all drafting, you must be able to measure. This means you have to know how to read a rule. It is surprising how few people ever learn to read a rule in the inch system. Now, however, you must be able to read a rule in the metric system as well.

HOW PEOPLE LEARNED TO MEASURE

People have always wanted to know the size of things. Hundreds of years ago this was difficult. There was no standard of measurement or way of measuring. According to history, the Romans invented the inch. They decided that an inch was to be the width of a grown man's thumb. Fig. 3-1. There is a story that King Alfred of England decided what the foot was to be. He said that a foot would be the distance from the heel to the toe of his own foot. He ordered a permanent stick made of iron to serve as a master yardstick of three feet, a standard

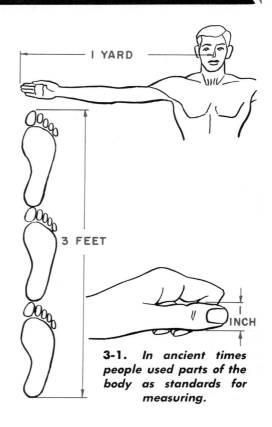

3-1. *In ancient times people used parts of the body as standards for measuring.*

for the entire kingdom. From "standards" like these, the English, or customary, system of measurement developed.

THE METRIC SYSTEM

In 1791, the French government adopted an entirely different standard of measurement called the metric system. This was based on a unit called the metre. In the metric system, all units are multiples of ten. For example, one metre equals ten decimetres, or one hundred centimetres, or one thousand millimetres.

Today, the United States still uses the customary, or English, system of measurement. It is the only major country that does so. Even the English have adopted metrics. However, the United States is now on its way toward becoming a metric nation. In doing so, we will adopt the SI Metric System. The abbreviation SI stands for "International System of Units," the modern metric system of measurement.

There are seven basic metric units. Although in beginning drawing you will need to know only about the metre, the chart in Fig. 3-2 lists all of the units for your information.

3-2. *This table describes the seven SI metric base units.*

BASE UNIT	SYMBOL	DEFINITION
metre (length)	m	The measure equal to a certain number of wavelengths of light given off by the krypton-86 atom.
kilogram (mass)	kg	The measure equal to the mass of the standard kilogram artifact located at the International Bureau of Weights and Measures in France. The kilogram is often used to measure weight.
second (time)	s	The measure equal to a certain number of oscillations (back and forth movements) of the cesium atom in an atomic clock.
ampere (electric current)	A	The measure equal to the amount of current in two wires a certain distance apart that results in a specific force between the two wires.
candela (luminous intensity)	cd	The measure equal to the amount of light given off by platinum at its freezing point. At its freezing point, platinum is hot and it glows.
mole (amount of substance)	mol	The measure equal to the number of particles contained in a certain amount of carbon. The mole is used only for very scientific measurements.
kelvin (temperature)	K	The measure of a certain fraction of the temperature of water at its triple point. The triple point of water is the temperature at which it exists as a solid, liquid, and vapor. The kelvin is used for special temperature measures. For practical purposes, the Celsius scale is used. The Celsius scale is 0 at the freezing point and 100 at the boiling point of water. Celsius replaces, but is equal to, the old centigrade scale.

Because we still use the English system, many of the dimensions in this book are in inches or fractions of an inch. However, the metric system is also used by many companies; so a system called "dual dimensioning" is sometimes used. This means that both the English and metric measurements are given. You should learn to read a rule in both systems accurately. The metric system is not difficult.

All that you need to know is that *milli* means one one-thousandth; *centi* means one one-hundredth; and *kilo* means one thousand. Because it is a decimal system, it is quite easy to learn. Figs. 3-3 and 3-4 are charts for converting measurements from one system to another.

READING A RULE

Most rules used in drawing are one

3-3. *Common conversions: customary to metric—metric to customary.*

LENGTH	
CUSTOMARY TO METRIC	**METRIC TO CUSTOMARY**
1 inch = 25.40 millimetres	1 millimetre = 0.03937 inch
1 inch = 2.540 centimetres	1 centimetre = 0.3937 inch
1 foot = 30.480 centimetres	1 metre = 39.37 inches
1 foot = 0.3048 metre	1 metre = 3.2808 feet
1 yard = 91.440 centimetres	1 metre = 1.0936 yards
1 yard = 0.9144 metre	1 kilometre = 0.62137 mile
1 mile = 1.609 kilometres	

AREA	
CUSTOMARY TO METRIC	**METRIC TO CUSTOMARY**
1 sq. inch = 645.16 sq. millimetres	1 sq. millimetre = 0.00155 sq. inch
1 sq. inch = 6.4516 sq. centimetres	1 sq. centimetre = 0.1550 sq. inch
1 sq. foot = 929.03 sq. centimetres	1 sq. metre = 10.7640 sq. feet
1 sq. foot = 0.0929 sq. metre	1 sq. metre = 1.196 sq. yards
1 sq. yard = 0.836 sq. metre	1 sq. hectometre = 2.471 acres
1 acre = 0.4047 sq. hectometre	1 hectare = 2.471 acres
1 acre = 0.4047 hectare	1 sq. kilometre = 0.386 sq. mile
1 sq. mile = 2.59 sq. kilometres	

MASS (Weight)	
CUSTOMARY TO METRIC	**METRIC TO CUSTOMARY**
1 ounce (dry) = 28.35 grams	1 gram = 0.03527 ounce
1 pound = 0.4536 kilogram	1 kilogram = 2.2046 pounds
1 short ton (2000 lb.) = 907.2 kilograms	1 metric ton = 2204.6 pounds
1 short ton (2000 lb.) = 0.9072 metric ton	1 metric ton = 1.102 tons (short)

VOLUME (Capacity)	
CUSTOMARY TO METRIC	**METRIC TO CUSTOMARY**
1 fluid ounce = 2.957 centilitres = 29.57 cm³*	1 centilitre = 10 cm³* = 0.338 fluid ounce
1 pint (liq.) = 4.732 decilitres = 473.2 cm³*	1 decilitre = 100 cm³* = 0.2114 pint (liq.)
1 quart (liq.) = 0.9463 litre = 0.9463 dm³**	1 litre = 1 dm³** = 1.0567 quarts (liq.)
1 gallon (liq.) = 3.7854 litres = 3.7854 dm³**	1 litre = 1 dm³** = 0.26417 gallon (liq.)

*cubic centimetre   **cubic decimetre

3-4. *Decimal and millimetre equivalents of parts of an inch.*

Fractional Inch	Decimal Inch	mm	Fractional Inch	Decimal Inch	mm	Fractional Inch	Decimal Inch	mm
	0.0039	0.1		0.0709	1.8		0.1614	4.1
	0.0079	0.2		0.0728	1.85		0.1654	4.2
	0.0118	0.3		0.0748	1.9		0.1673	4.25
1/64	0.0156			0.0768	1.95		0.1693	4.3
	0.0157	0.4	5/64	0.0781		11/64	0.1719	
	0.0165	0.42		0.0787	2.0		0.1732	4.4
	0.0173	0.44		0.0807	2.05		0.1772	4.5
	0.0177	0.45		0.0827	2.1		0.1811	4.6
	0.0181	0.46		0.0846	2.15		0.1850	4.7
	0.0189	0.48		0.0866	2.2		0.1870	4.75
	0.0197	0.5		0.0886	2.25		0.1875	
	0.0217	0.55		0.0906	2.3	3/16	0.1890	4.8
	0.0236	0.6		0.0925	2.35		0.1929	4.9
	0.0256	0.65	3/32	0.0938			0.1969	5.0
	0.0276	0.7		0.0945	2.4		0.2008	5.1
	0.0295	0.75		0.0965	2.45	13/64	0.2031	
1/32	0.0312			0.0981	2.5		0.2047	5.2
	0.0315	0.8		0.1024	2.6		0.2067	5.25
	0.0335	0.85		0.1063	2.7		0.2087	5.3
	0.0354	0.9		0.1083	2.75		0.2126	5.4
	0.0374	0.95	7/64	0.1094			0.2165	5.5
	0.0394	1.0		0.1102	2.8	7/32	0.2188	
	0.0413	1.05		0.1142	2.9		0.2205	5.6
	0.0433	1.1		0.1181	3.0		0.2244	5.7
	0.0453	1.15		0.1220	3.1		0.2264	5.75
3/64	0.0469		1/8	0.1250			0.2283	5.8
	0.0472	1.2		0.1260	3.2		0.2323	5.9
	0.0492	1.25		0.1280	3.25	15/64	0.2344	
	0.0512	1.3		0.1299	3.3		0.2362	6.0
	0.0531	1.35		0.1339	3.4		0.2402	6.1
	0.0551	1.4		0.1378	3.5		0.2441	6.2
	0.0571	1.45	9/64	0.1406			0.2461	6.25
	0.0591	1.5		0.1417	3.6		0.2480	6.3
	0.0610	1.55		0.1457	3.7	1/4	0.2500	
1/16	0.0625			0.1476	3.75		0.2520	6.4
	0.0630	1.6		0.1496	3.8		0.2559	6.5
	0.0650	1.65		0.1535	3.9		0.2598	6.6
	0.0669	1.7	5/32	0.1562			0.2638	6.7
	0.0689	1.75		0.1575	4.0	17/64	0.2656	

3-4. Cont'd.

Frac-tional Inch	Dec-imal Inch	mm	Frac-tional Inch	Dec-imal Inch	mm	Frac-tional Inch	Dec-imal Inch	mm
	0.2657	6.75		0.3740	9.5		0.6693	17.0
	0.2677	6.8	3/8	0.3750		43/64	0.6719	
	0.2717	6.9		0.3780	9.6	11/16	0.6875	
	0.2756	7.0		0.3819	9.7		0.6890	17.5
	0.2795	7.1		0.3839	9.75	45/64	0.7031	
9/32	0.2812			0.3858	9.8		0.7087	18.0
	0.2835	7.2		0.3898	9.9	23/32	0.7188	
	0.2854	7.25	25/64	0.3906			0.7283	18.5
	0.2874	7.3		0.3937	10.0	47/64	0.7344	
	0.2913	7.4	13/32	0.4062			0.7480	19.0
	0.2953	7.5		0.4134	10.5	3/4	0.7500	
19/64	0.2969		27/64	0.4219		49/64	0.7656	
	0.2992	7.6		0.4331	11.0		0.768	19.5
	0.3031	7.7	7/16	0.4375		25/32	0.7812	
	0.3051	7.75		0.4528	11.5		0.7874	20.0
	0.3071	7.8	29/64	0.4531		51/64	0.7969	
	0.3110	7.9	15/32	0.4688			0.808	20.5
5/16	0.3125			0.4724	12.0	13/16	0.8125	
	0.3150	8.0	31/64	0.4844			0.8268	21.0
	0.3189	8.1		0.4921	12.5	53/64	0.8281	
	0.3228	8.2	1/2	0.5000		27/32	0.8437	
	0.3248	8.25		0.5118	13.0		0.847	21.5
	0.3268	8.3	33/64	0.5156		55/64	0.8594	
21/64	0.3281		17/32	0.5312			0.8661	22.0
	0.3307	8.4		0.5315	13.5	7/8	0.8750	
	0.3346	8.5	35/64	0.5469			0.886	22.5
	0.3386	8.6		0.5512	14.0	57/64	0.8906	
	0.3425	8.7	9/16	0.5625			0.9055	23.0
11/32	0.3438			0.5709	14.5	29/32	0.9062	
	0.3445	8.75	37/64	0.5781		59/64	0.9219	
	0.3465	8.8		0.5906	15.0		0.926	23.5
	0.3504	8.9	19/32	0.5938		15/16	0.9375	
	0.3543	9.0	39/64	0.6094			0.9449	24.0
	0.3583	9.1		0.6102	15.5	61/64	0.9531	
23/64	0.3594		5/8	0.6250			0.965	24.5
	0.3622	9.2		0.6299	16.0	31/32	0.9687	
	0.3642	9.25	41/64	0.6406			0.9843	25.0
	0.3661	9.3		0.6496	16.5	63/64	0.9844	
	0.3701	9.4	21/32	0.6562		64/64	1.0000	25.4

foot, or twelve inches, long in the English system. The measurements are usually given in feet, inches, and parts of an inch. You should not find it hard to measure feet in exact inches. You already know that there are twelve inches in a foot and three feet, or thirty-six inches, in a yard. In the metric system, the measurement is even easier. There are ten millimetres in one centimetre, a hundred centimetres in one metre, and a thousand metres in one kilometre.

Let's take a look at the chart shown in Fig. 3-5, below. It is in the English system. The distance between 0 and 1 is one inch. At line A you see that the inch is divided into two equal

parts. Each half is one-half inch ($1/2"$). On a rule, this half-inch division line is the longest line between the inch marks. At line B the inch is divided into four equal parts. The first line is $1/4$ inch; the second line is $2/4$, or $1/2$, inch; the third line is $3/4$ inch. At line C, you will notice that the inch is divided into eight equal parts so that each small division is one-eighth inch ($1/8"$). Two of these divisions make $2/8$, or $1/4$, inch (as shown on line B). Four of these divisions make $4/8$ inch, or $2/4$ inch, or $1/2$ inch ($1/2"$). At line D, the inch is divided into 16 parts. This is usually the smallest division found on rules used in drawing. Notice again that $4/16"$ is equal to $2/8"$, or $1/4"$. One line past $1/4"$ is equal to $5/16"$. You will see on your rule that between each one-inch mark, the half-inch mark is the longest one. The quarter-inch mark is the next longest, the eighth-inch mark the next, and the sixteenth-inch mark is the shortest.

To read a part or fraction of an inch, count the number of small divisions beyond the last inch mark. For example, when measuring the line in Fig. 3-6, you will find that it is 2" plus 4 small divisions. This is $4/16"$, which is the same as $2/8"$ or $1/4"$. The line measures $2 1/4"$. One small division past $1/2"$ would be $9/16"$ ($8/16 + 1/16$).

3-5. *Chart showing how the inch is divided into smaller and smaller units.*

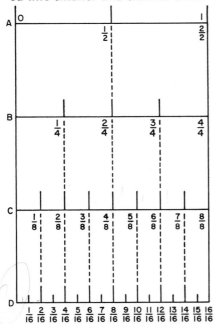

3-6. *Use a rule to measure this line. It is $2 1/4"$ long, isn't it?*

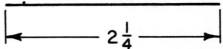

Now let's look at a metric rule. Fig. 3-7. Here you see that the rule is divided into centimetres. Each centimetre is divided into 10 smaller divisions called millimetres. The smallest division on the inch was $^1/_{16}$, which is 1.59 millimetres. To help you learn how to use both the customary and the metric systems, several of the drawings in this book are done in dual dimensioning. If you wish to add dual dimensioning to your own drawings, you should place the customary dimension first and then place the metric dimension either directly after or below it. Fig. 3-8. Some other examples of dual dimensioning are shown throughout the book. Wherever you see the second dimension shown in parentheses or brackets, this will be the measurement in millimetres. To convert fractions to millimetres use the table that is shown on pages 25 and 26.

In Fig. 3-9 you will find a sample metric measuring problem. Measure the line with a metric rule. Note that the length of this line is 4 centimetres plus 7 millimetres. One millimetre equals $^1/_{10}$ of a centimetre. The line is therefore 4 and $^7/_{10}$ centimetres, or 4.7 cm, long. However, most drawings will be measured in millimetres. The line is 47 millimetres long.

TOOLS AND MATERIALS

For a first activity in drawing you will need four things:
- Rule.
- Pencil.
- Eraser.
- Sheet of plain white paper.

Here is what you should know about rules and pencils:

Rules. In beginning drawing an inexpensive 12″ wood rule is all that is needed. This is the kind you use at home and in school. In more advanced drawing you might use the architect's scale. You will find more information about this and other scales in Unit 8.

Pencils. Pencils are made in many grades of hardness. The harder the pencil, the lighter the line it makes. The lead of a pencil is made of graphite, clay, and wax. The more clay it contains, the harder the lead. Pencils

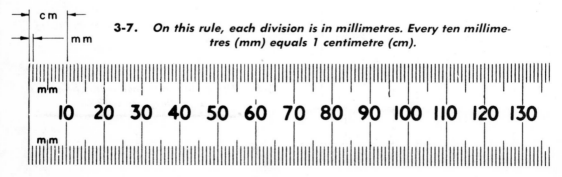

3-7. *On this rule, each division is in millimetres. Every ten millimetres (mm) equals 1 centimetre (cm).*

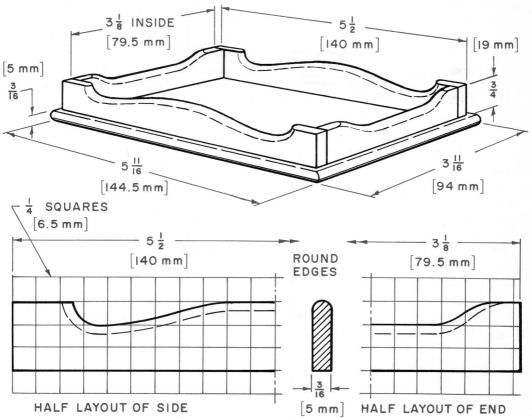

3 1/8 INSIDE
[79.5 mm]

5 1/2
[140 mm]

[19 mm]

[5 mm]

3/16

3/4

5 11/16
[144.5 mm]

3 11/16
[94 mm]

1/4 SQUARES
[6.5 mm]

5 1/2
[140 mm]

ROUND
EDGES

3 1/8
[79.5 mm]

3/16

HALF LAYOUT OF SIDE

[5 mm]

HALF LAYOUT OF END

3-8. *An example of dual dimensioning. Other examples are shown in Unit 13.*

used by drafters are numbered from 9H (very hard) to 6B (extremely soft). The ordinary writing pencils are numbered 1, 2, and 3. Number 3 is hardest and is equal to 2H; 2 is equal to HB, and 1 is about the same as 2B. You should use an H, 2H, or No. 3 pencil. The number or grade is stamped on the pencil. Always sharpen the end away from the grade stamp. This is important so that you will always know the kind of pencil you are using.

The simplest way to remove the wood is to use a pencil sharpener. A knife can also be used. The pencil should be sharpened to a shape shown in Fig. 3-10 (P. 30). To keep a cone-shaped point on the lead, rotate the pencil slowly as you rub the point

3-9. *Use a metric rule to measure this line. You will find that it is 47 mm long.*

47 mm

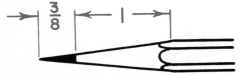

3-10. *A pencil point correctly sharpened.*

on a small sandpaper pad. Fig. 3-11. Always keep the lead sharp. You can also use a fine file to do this. WARNING: Be sure to keep the dirt away from your drawing board or paper. Hold the pencil about 1¹/₂″ from the point between your thumb, forefinger, and third finger. Slant the pencil in the direction you move it, at an angle of about 60 degrees. Rotate the pencil slightly as you draw the lines. Fig. 3-12. This will keep it sharp longer, and you won't flatten out the lead so fast. You will also get a sharper and more accurate line.

DRAWING A STRAIGHT LINE

Can you draw a straight line of a certain length with a rule and pencil?

3-11. *Using a sandpaper pad or pencil pointer to keep the point of the lead sharp. The felt at the end removes the dust after the pencil is sharpened.*

You can't make drawings until you can do this simple but important thing. Be sure the rule is in good condition. Hold the rule firmly against the paper. Mark a point at the zero line on the rule. Mark another point at the other end of the line. For example, if you want to draw a line 3⁵/₈″ long, place the second point at exactly 3″ plus 10 small divisions (3¹⁰/₁₆″). Place the point of the pencil at the zero mark. Hold the lead firmly against the edge of the rule. Move the pencil, turning it slightly, until the other point is reached. Stop exactly at the second point.

MEASURING

Now let's show that you can measure accurately. Here are some lines

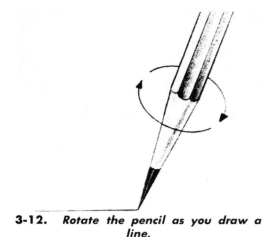

3-12. *Rotate the pencil as you draw a line.*

that represent the diameter, thickness, width, or length of some common things you may see every day. Fig. 3-13. Hold the zero mark of the rule at one end of the line. What is its length? NOTE: Always reduce the fraction to the smallest denominator possible. If it is $^{12}/_{16}''$, it should be written $^3/_4''$. Find out what the length of each line is and write it on a piece of paper. Measure to the nearest $^1/_{16}''$. Use a metric scale to measure these lines in millimetres. Measure to the nearest millimetre.

3-13. *Measure these lines with customary and metric scales. Then look through this list to find what common items they represent.*

Width of a business envelope: $4^1/_8''$ (105 mm)
Length of an 8-cent postage stamp: $1''$ (25 mm)
Diameter of a fifty-cent piece: $1^3/_{16}''$ (30 mm)
Width of a dollar bill: $2^9/_{16}''$ (65 mm)
Diameter of a quart paint can: $4^3/_{16}''$ (107 mm)
Width of a hacksaw blade: $^1/_2''$ (13 mm)
Width of an electrical switch plate: $2^3/_4''$ (70 mm)
Thickness of a 2 × 4 (green lumber): $1^9/_{16}''$ (40 mm)
Width of a 2 × 4 (dry lumber): $3^1/_2''$ (89 mm)

Unit 4. Drawing Vertical and Horizontal Lines

COMMON TOOLS AND MATERIALS

Drawing Bench. Drafters do their work at benches similar to those in Fig. 4-1. Paper can be fastened directly to it. The bench is a convenient height to make the drawing position comfortable.

A drawing bench is not necessary, however. Good drawings can be made in the school lab or at home on a shop bench or ordinary table.

Sometimes a stand can be used to hold the drawing board.

Drawing Board. A drawing board is made of some softwood, such as basswood or white pine. The surface must be smooth and the edges straight. Most boards are made of several horizontal pieces with a vertical piece (cleat) at either end. This cleat provides a smooth edge for the T square. Drawing boards come in various sizes from 12″ × 17″ to

4-1. *A corner of a modern industrial arts drawing room.*

4-2. *Parts of a T square: A. Head. B. Blade. Use a T square with great care. Never drop it or use it as a pounding tool. It is important that the head and blade be tight for good work.*

31″ × 42″. The common size is 18″ × 24″. You do not need a drawing board if a drawing bench is available. At home or in the shop a rectangular piece of ³/₄″ plywood will make a suitable board.

T Square. The T square has a head and a blade that are fastened at right angles. Fig. 4-2. The more expensive kinds have a transparent edge on either side of the blade. The T square is used to draw all *horizontal* lines. With a *triangle* and a *T square* you

can draw *vertical* and *slanted* or *inclined* lines.

To use a T square, place the head against the *left* edge of the drawing board or bench. Apply slight inward pressure to the blade with your left hand. Fig. 4-3. The head should always be held against the edge of the board. The T square can then be slid up and down to draw horizontal lines at any location. *If you are left-handed,* (and one in ten persons is), just reverse this position. Place the head of the T square against the right edge and apply pressure with your right hand. Fig. 4-4.

Triangles. There are two right triangles used in drawing. One is called a 45-degree triangle and the other a 30-60 degree triangle. These triangles are transparent and come in various sizes. An 8″, 10″, or 12″ triangle is a good size to have. You will learn a good deal about triangles in the next unit.

Triangles are used to draw *vertical* lines. If you are right-handed, place the triangle as shown in Fig. 4-5,

4-3. *The correct method for using the T square if you are right-handed. Note that the pressure is applied inward with the left hand. Hold the pencil at an angle of about 60 degrees to the paper.*

4-4. *The correct method of using the T square if you are left-handed.*

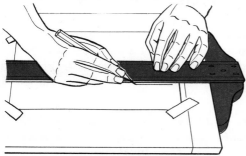

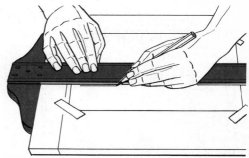

4-5. *Drawing a vertical line with a triangle. One hand holds the T square and triangle. Note that the pencil is held at an angle of about 60 degrees. The line is drawn from the bottom to the top.*

4-6. *Left-hand view of same procedure.*

with the tapered side toward your right hand. Reverse this if you are left-handed. Fig. 4-6. Apply slight inward pressure to the blade of the T square with your thumb and little finger. Hold the triangle firmly against the upper edge of the T square blade with your other fingers. Now you can slide the triangle to the right or left. You can also move both the triangle and T square up and down with one hand. Try this.

Paper. Drawing paper is made in four colors: white, cream, light green, and buff. It comes in various weights,

or sheet thicknesses, and in many different sizes. The most common are $8\frac{1}{2}'' \times 11''$, $11'' \times 17''$, and $17'' \times 22''$. You will probably use sheets $8\frac{1}{2}'' \times 11''/$ or cut the sheets from $11'' \times 17''$ paper on a paper cutter. Metric paper sizes are shown in Figs. 4-7 and 4-8.

Drafter's Tape and Thumbtacks. There are two ways of fastening the paper in place. The best way is to use four pieces of masking tape (drafter's tape across the corners. The tape can be used over and over again and will not harm the board or paper. Some drafters still use thumbtacks. In time these will mar the surface of the board or table, however.

Erasers. There are two common kinds of erasers: red rubber erasers and yellow art gum erasers. These are used to correct mistakes and to remove light layout lines. The best kind

"A" PAPER SIZES		
	millimetres	inches (approx.)
A0	841 × 1189	$33\frac{1}{8} \times 46\frac{3}{4}$
A1	594 × 841	$23\frac{3}{8} \times 33\frac{1}{8}$
A2	420 × 594	$16\frac{1}{2} \times 23\frac{3}{8}$
A3	297 × 420	$11\frac{3}{4} \times 16\frac{1}{2}$
A4	210 × 297	$8\frac{1}{4} \times 11\frac{3}{4}$
A5	148 × 210	$5\frac{7}{8} \times 8\frac{1}{4}$
A6	105 × 148	$4\frac{1}{8} \times 5\frac{7}{8}$

4-7. *Table of metric paper sizes. You will probably use the A4 paper size as it becomes available.*

ISO - A SIZE PAPER

1189 mm x 841 mm : 1 SQUARE METRE

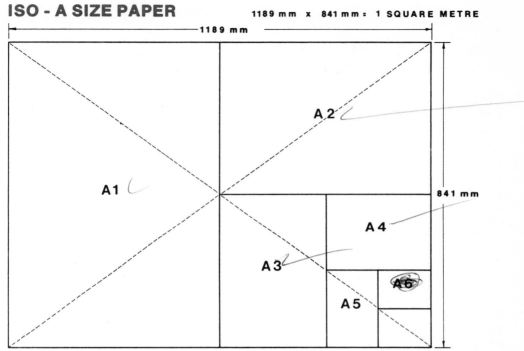

4-8. *This illustration shows the relationships of the various metric drafting paper sizes.*

is the red eraser. To erase lines, first clean the eraser on a piece of paper. Hold the paper firmly to the board and rub with short strokes. Brush the dirt away with a clean cloth or a brush. An eraser shield is very helpful. Fig. 4-9. Choose the correct opening and place it over the line to be erased. Hold the shield with one hand and rub across the opening with the eraser.

GETTING STARTED ON A SIMPLE DRAWING

1. Wipe the top of the table or drawing board with a clean cloth. Also wipe each of the tools to be sure they have no dust or dirt on them.

Wash your hands. Be careful after you sharpen pencils to keep the dirt off your fingers. You will find that neatness is important in drawing.

4-9. *An eraser shield can be used to help in erasing a line.*

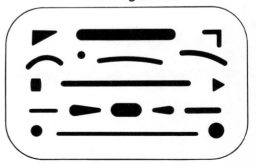

2. Choose a piece of paper 8½″ × 11″ or cut one to size. Place the paper on the drawing surface with the long side vertical or horizontal.

3. Hold the T square low against the edge of the board. Place the paper against the upper edge. See that one edge of the paper is about 2″ away from the edge of the board. Cut or tear off four pieces of masking tape. Place them across the corners so that about a half inch of each corner is covered.

4. You are now ready to make a layout for your first drawing. To measure any length along a horizontal line, place the rule even (flush with the upper edge of the blade of the T square. With a sharp pencil make a small light dot at the zero point on the rule and another at the correct length. To measure for a vertical line, hold the rule against the edge of a triangle and do the same. To make a dot or mark, put the point of the pencil at the correct position and twist it slightly between your fingers.

5. To draw a horizontal line, hold the pencil as shown in Fig. 4-3 or 4-4. Slide the T square up until the dots or marks are directly above the upper edge of the blade. Tilt the pencil so that the point is in the corner formed by blade and paper. Start at one dot and draw the pencil along from left to right, turning it slightly as you go. Apply even pressure. Slide the pencil hand along the T square with the little finger acting as a rest. Don't press so hard that a groove is made in the paper. This will make a very coarse line. Don't hold the pencil so lightly that the line is difficult to see. You want a nice, clean, sharp line that is easy to read. Start and stop exactly at the ends of the lines. Turning the pencil will keep the point sharp longer.

6. To draw a vertical line, hold the triangle against the T square with its edge directly over the dots. Draw the line from the bottom dot upward in the same way. Fig. 4-5 or 4-6. Be sure to hold the T square and triangle firmly in place. If you don't, the triangle may slide or the T square may tip slightly.

Unit 5. Drawing Inclined (Slanted) Lines and Angles

TRIANGLES

A triangle is a three-sided figure. Fig. 5-1. Those used as tools in drawing are the 45-degree and the 30-60 degree triangles. The 45-degree triangle has one right angle (90 degrees) and two that are 45 degrees, making a total of 180 degrees. The

30-60 degree triangle also has one right angle, one that is 30 degrees, and a third that is 60 degrees, also totaling 180 degrees.

KINDS OF ANGLES

If an angle is exactly 90 degrees, it is a *right* angle. Fig. 5-2A. If it is less than 90 degrees, it is an *acute* angle. Fig. 5-2B. When it is more than 90 degrees, it is an *obtuse* angle. Fig. 5-2C.

5-1. *How many triangles can you see in this sailboat?*

DRAWING ANGLES

You can use triangles to draw lines at various angles to the horizontal and vertical line. To draw a 45-degree angle, place the 45-degree triangle against the upper edge of the T square. Hold the two tools firmly to the paper with one hand and draw the line as shown in Fig. 5-3 (P. 38). The direction in which the line is drawn is shown with an arrow. Notice that the line will be at an angle of 45 degrees to both horizontal and vertical. In Fig. 5-4, the 30-60 degree triangle is used to draw a line at 30 degrees to the horizontal and 60 degrees to the

5-2. *Kinds of angles: A. Right. B. Acute. C. Obtuse.*

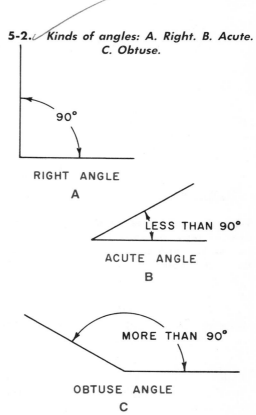

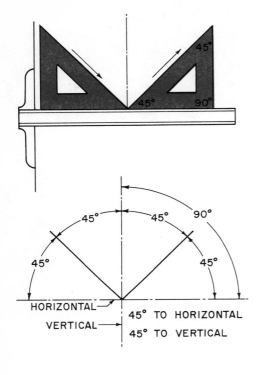

5-3. *Drawing lines at an angle of 45 degrees. Note the arrow showing the direction for drawing the lines. The square and the circle show lines at an angle of 45 degrees.*

a circle divided into 15-degree segments. (The triangles were used in the different positions shown in Fig. 5-3 to Fig. 5-7. With a little practice you will find it easy to use the triangle in every position). Fig. 5-9 shows how to use the 30-60 degree triangle to lay out a clock face.

DRAWING PARALLEL LINES

To draw a line parallel to another line, place one edge of the triangle in

5-4. *Drawing lines at an angle of 30 degrees to the horizontal.*

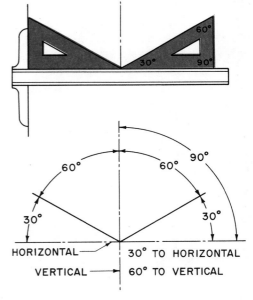

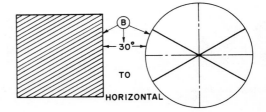

vertical. By using this triangle in the other position, Fig. 5-5, these angles can be reversed. By using the two triangles together as shown in Fig. 5-6 and 5-7 (P. 40), you can obtain angles of 15 and 75 degrees. Fig. 5-8 shows

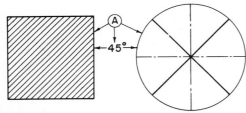

line with the first line. Fig. 5-10 (P. 41). As a guide, slide the T square up the triangle. Then slip the triangle along and draw the second line.

DRAWING PERPENDICULAR LINES

To draw a line perpendicular to another line, hold the triangle against

5-5. *Drawing lines at an angle of 60 degrees to the horizontal.*

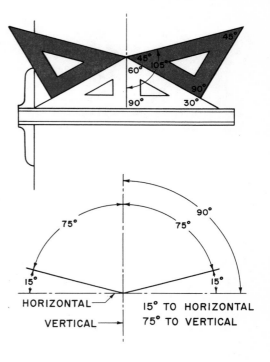

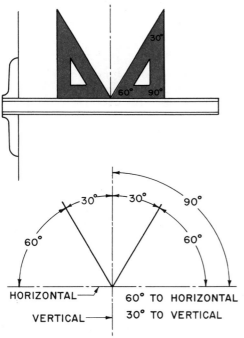

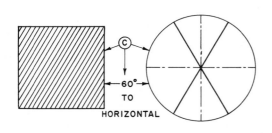

the T square as shown in Fig. 5-11. Draw the first line. Now slide the triangle over and draw the second line to intersect the first.

PROTRACTOR

A protractor is a drawing tool made of metal or plastic and shaped like a

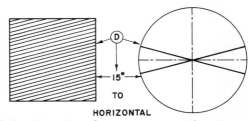

5-6. *Drawing lines at an angle of 15 degrees to the horizontal. Notice how the two triangles are used together to do this.*

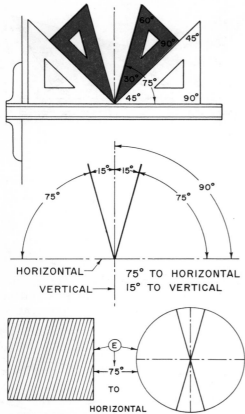

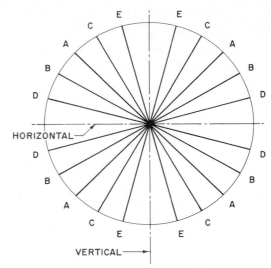

5-7. *Drawing a line at an angle of 75 degrees to the horizontal. See how the two triangles are used.*

5-8. *A circle divided into 15-degree segments. Each letter around the circle is the same as the line shown by the letters in Figs. 5-3 to 5-7. For example, B is a line drawn at an angle of 30 degrees to the horizontal, as shown in Fig. 5-4.*

half circle. It is used to lay out odd angles (those other than multiples of 15). The scale on the outer edge is divided into degrees running from 0 to 180 from *left to right* or from *right to left*. The scale just inside that runs from 0 to 180 degrees in the opposite direction.

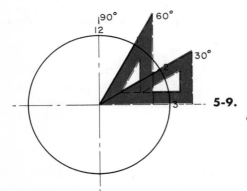

5-9. *Using a 30-60 degree triangle to lay out the position of a clock face.*

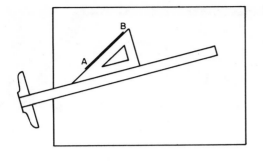

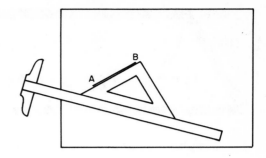

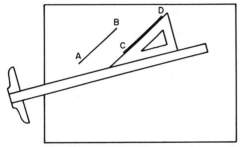

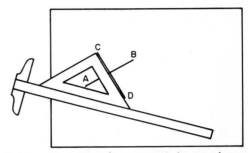

5-10. *Drawing parallel lines. (Left-handed person—reverse sides.) AB is drawn first. Then the triangle is slid along the T square and line CD drawn.*

5-11. *Drawing lines at right angles to each other. (Left-handed person—reverse sides.) AB is drawn first, then the 45-degree triangle slid to the left and line CD drawn.*

To lay out an angle, draw a horizontal or vertical line. Place the straight edge of the protractor on the line. The center of the protractor should be at a point marked on the line where the angle is to be drawn. Find the correct angle on the scale and mark a point. Now use a straightedge instrument to finish drawing the angle. See Fig. 5-12, below.

5-12. *Using a protractor to lay out a 36-degree angle.*

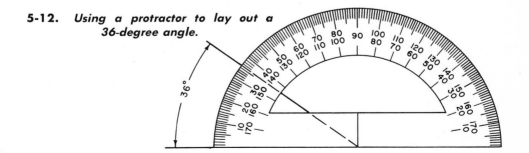

Unit 6. Drawing Circles, Arcs, and Irregular Curves

It's often been said that the wheel is our greatest invention. Without it we wouldn't have bicycles, cars, trains, or anything mechanical. The wheel is only one item that is drawn in the shape of a circle. Can you name some more?

The *diameter* of a circle is the length of a straight line through the center. The *radius* is half the diameter. The *circumference* is the distance around the outside. Fig. 6-1. An *arc* is a part of a circle. A line is *tangent* to a circle when it touches the outside but does not cross it. Fig. 6-2.

Circles are usually drawn with a compass.

KINDS OF COMPASSES

On all compasses one leg is a metal point. There are several kinds of compasses. The simplest is a *pencil compass*. The second leg has an opening for a pencil. (Fig. 6-4.) Use an H or 2H pencil, sharpened to a cone-shaped point, on a pencil compass. On a *drawing compass* a piece of lead fits into the second leg. Sharpen this point to a wedge shape. Adjust the compass so that the metal point is about ¹/₃₂″ longer than the lead point. Compasses can also be classified according to the type of joint.

LOCATING THE CENTER OF CIRCLES

Before drawing a circle, draw two intersecting lines to form the center. These lines are made up of a long dash, a space, a short dash, a space, and a long dash. Fig. 6-3. Such a line is called a *center line*. The center line is used to locate the center of all circles and arcs and to divide an

6-1.   *The parts of a circle.*

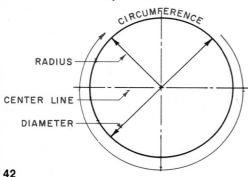

6-2.   *A line tangent to a circle.*

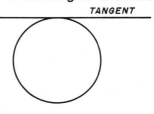

6-3. *The correct way of drawing a center line. This is drawn as a fine, light line.*

object that is equal on both sides (symmetrical). (On small circles or arcs, only two small dashes are used.)

ADJUSTING THE COMPASS

Place a rule or scale on a piece of scrap paper. Never place the point of the compass on the rule itself. Hold the point of the compass at the zero mark of the rule. Next open the compass until the measurement shows the correct radius. Then test the compass by turning a small arc on scrap paper. Measure from the center to the arc to check the radius.

DRAWING CIRCLES

Place the point of the compass over the center of the circle. Hold the top of the compass between the thumb, forefinger, and third finger. Tip the compass slightly toward yourself and turn it clockwise. Fig. 6-4. (Left-

handed persons—turn counter-clockwise.) Apply just enough pressure all the time to make a clear, sharp line. If you apply too much pressure the legs may spread, ruining the circle. Don't go over the line too often. Make sure that the line made by your compass looks the same in thickness as other straight lines drawn with a pencil.

DRAWING ARCS

An arc is often used as a part of a drawing to show a round corner. The arc is tangent to two lines at 90 degrees. To draw this proceed as follows:

1. Draw very light construction lines to represent the straight lines that intersect.

2. Measure in from these lines an amount equal to the radius of the arc. Draw two lines that are parallel to the first lines to locate the center for the arc (0).

3. Adjust the compass to the correct radius, using 0 as the center. Draw the arc from one straight line to the next. Try to make a sharp, clean curve. Fig. 6-5.

4. Go over the straight lines again with a pencil to darken them, if necessary. The line of the arc and the

6-4. *Using a pencil compass.*

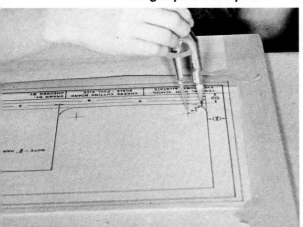

6-5. *An arc to form a rounded corner.*

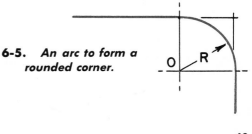

straight line should appear to be the same weight. Also, make sure the straight line joins the arc without overlapping.

To draw a figure in which arcs of two different radii (more than one radius) are joined with straight lines, proceed as follows (Fig. 6-6):

1. Draw the arcs at either end, using a light line.

2. Place the straightedge or rule just touching the circumference of both arcs.

3. Hold a triangle against this straightedge. Slide it along until the right angle it makes with the straight-edge passes through the center of the arc. Mark this position on the circum-

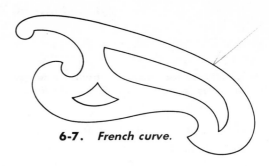

6-7. French curve.

ference. This is the point of tangency. Do this on both sides of both arcs.

4. Darken the arcs. Then draw the straight lines connecting the points of tangency.

DRAWING IRREGULAR CURVES

Many projects have irregular curves, especially those in metal and

6-6. Notice how the points of tangency are located with a straightedge and triangles.

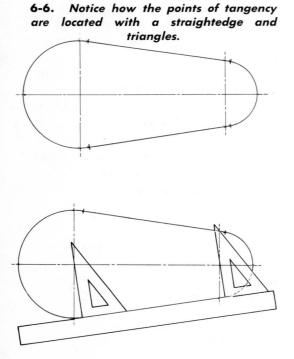

6-8. Using a French curve.

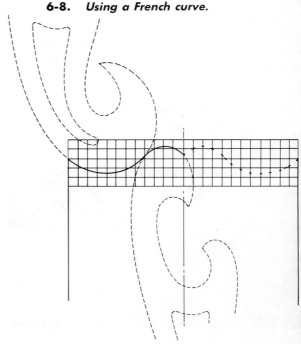

wood. To draw these use a French, or irregular, curve. This is a plastic device made in several shapes and sizes. Fig. 6-7. Different places on the curve duplicate different curved shapes. To draw an irregular curve, first locate the several points that the curve is to follow. The more points the better. It is a good idea to sketch a freehand curve that roughly follows those points. Now, use the French curve. By trial and error *move the curve until three points are in contact with it.* Fig. 6-8. Draw this curved section not quite up to the outside points. Move the curve to the next three points and repeat. You will need to slide the device around each time to find the proper curvature.

Unit 7. Drawing to Scale

Would you like to take a ride on this motorcycle? Fig. 7-1. It looks real enough to be a full-size bike. Actually, however, it is a model made to a scale of ⅛″ to the foot (⅛″ = 1′0″). Many objects are too large to draw full size. For example, you couldn't make a full-size drawing of the state you live in or your school's football field. A drawing does not have to be full size to make it completely useful. The *lines* show the *shape* of the object and the *dimensions* tell the size. Drawings that are made larger or smaller than full size are called *scale drawings.* Notice various balls used in sports. Fig. 7-2 (P. 46). The marble, is drawn *double size,* the golf ball to *full size,* and the others to smaller scales. Scale drawings can be made with an ordinary rule. If you are using an architects scale, however, be sure to study Unit 8.

7-1. *This scale model looks like the real thing.*

MAKING A SCALE DRAWING

To make a scale drawing with an ordinary rule proceed as follows:

1. Determine the scale to use. Suppose you wish to make a drawing of this metal wastepaper basket. Fig. 7-3. It is 10″ in diameter and 12″ high. It would be impossible to make it full

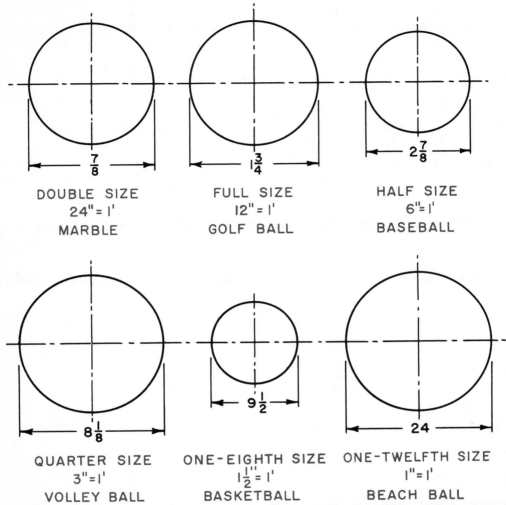

DOUBLE SIZE
24"= 1'
MARBLE

FULL SIZE
12"= 1'
GOLF BALL

HALF SIZE
6"= 1'
BASEBALL

QUARTER SIZE
3"= 1'
VOLLEY BALL

ONE-EIGHTH SIZE
$1\frac{1}{2}$" = 1'
BASKETBALL

ONE-TWELFTH SIZE
1"= 1'
BEACH BALL

7-2. *Scale drawings of several kinds of balls. Note that by using different scales the balls appear to be of similar size. The dimensions, however, tell the real story.*

size on an 8½" × 11" sheet of paper. If you make it half size (6" equals 1', or 6" = 1'0"), it will fit very nicely on the paper. Fig. 7-4. A wastebasket 250 mm in diameter (about 10") and 300 mm high (about 12") could also be drawn half size. The metric scale to use would be 1 mm = 2 mm. Al-

ways make the scale as large as possible so the drawing will look well on the paper.

2. Make the scale drawing. In this drawing every inch is drawn ½" long, every ½" is drawn ¼", etc. To lay out the height of the basket (12"), measure 6" on your rule. To lay out the diameter of the basket, measure 5″. Follow this technique for all measurements.

OTHER SCALE DRAWINGS

The larger the object, the smaller the scale you need. Suppose you want to draw a football field. The field is 160 feet wide and 360 feet long. To get this on 8½″ × 11″ paper, you will need a scale of $^1/_{16}$″ equals 1 yard (3 feet). This will mean that the field is drawn 7½″ long. The 10-yard markers will be $^5/_8$″ apart. Your instructor will help you with scale on this kind of drawing.

Suppose you wish to make a layout of your room at home. This is often done on squared paper that has four or eight squares to the inch. A convenient scale then would be $^1/_2$″ equals 1 foot. If your room is 8′ × 12′, the actual size of the drawing will be 4″ × 6″. On a larger room you might use a scale of $^1/_4$″ = 1′.

POINTS TO REMEMBER

1. When using an ordinary foot rule to measure with, follow one of these common scales:

7-4. *A scale drawing of the wastepaper basket.*

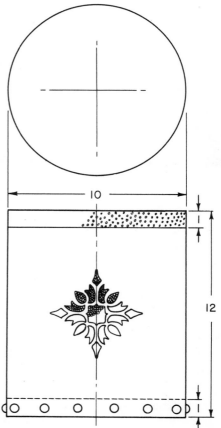

7-3. *Wastepaper basket.*

a. 24 inches equals 1 foot—double size (24″ = 1′).

b. 12 inches equals 1 foot—full size (12″ = 1′).

c. 6 inches equals 1 foot—half size (6″ = 1′).

d. 3 inches equals 1 foot—quarter size (3″ = 1′).

e. 1 inch equals 1 foot—one-twelfth size (1″ = 1′).

f. ¹/₂ inch equals 1 foot—one twenty-fourth size (¹/₂″ = 1′).

g. ¹/₄ inch equals 1 foot—one forty-eighth size (¹/₄″ = 1′).

When using an ordinary metric rule (in millimetres), use these scales:

a. 2 mm = 1 mm—double size.

b. 1 mm = 1 mm—full size.

c. 1 mm = 2 mm—half size.

d. 1 mm = 4 mm—quarter size.

e. 1mm = 10 mm—one-tenth size.

2. Make sure you indicate on the record strip or title block the scale used on the drawing.

3. Remember that the people who use your drawing to make something *never* measure the drawing itself. They always follow the dimensions that you have indicated on the drawing.

Unit 8. Drawing Instruments & Equipment

You have already learned that good drawings can be made with very simple tools. These elementary tools are found in all shops and most homes. But for drafters, engineers, architects, designers, and others who plan a career in drafting, instrument sets and other equipment are available.

DRAWING SETS

A set of instruments for drawing is usually purchased in a leather or plastic case. These matched sets range from the very simple with a few tools to very complete ones with several different sizes in each tool. A typical student drafting set would include the instruments shown in Fig. 8-1.

COMPASSES

A compass is used to draw circles and arcs. There are two types—the *friction-joint* and the *spring-joint*. The friction-joint, or adjustable leg, must be pulled open and pushed closed by hand. The joint should be tight enough to open and close under moderate pressure. This can be adjusted with a small screw at the joint.

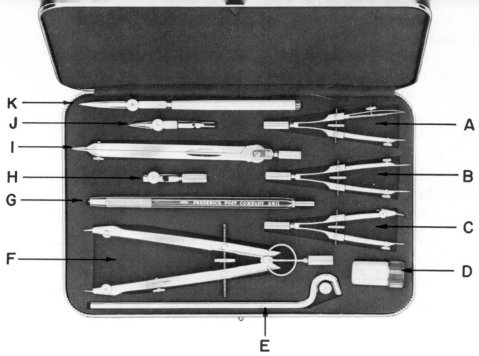

K ← J ← I ← H ← G ← F ← → A → B → C → D E

8-1. *A typical set of drafting instruments. A. Small ink compass. B. Small dividers. C. Small drawing compass. D. Lead pointer. E. Extension bar. F. Bow compass. G. Pencil. H. Extension bar adapter. I. Large dividers. J. Pen point. K. Ruling pen.*

If the compass works too hard, it is difficult to adjust it accurately. If it works too loosely, the legs may spread when a circle or arc is being made. The spring-joint compass, sometimes called a large bow, or center wheel compass, has a knurled nut attached to a screw thread be-tween the legs that is turned to open and close the compass. Fig. 8-2.

Bow Compass. This is a smaller spring-type compass used for drawing circles less than 2½" in diameter.

Dividers. Dividers are used to lay off equal distances on a straight or curved line, to transfer measure-

8-2. *A spring-joint compass, sometimes called a large bow, or center wheel, compass.*

ments, and to divide a line into equal parts. They are similar to a compass except that they have two metal points. To lay off equal distances, adjust the dividers to the correct length. Start at one point and step off the first space. Then rotate the dividers a half turn to lay off the others. Fig. 8-3. To transfer measurements, set the dividers on the first measurement and then move the dividers to the new position. To divide a line into equal parts, adjust the dividers by trial and error and space off the line. Readjust until the desired number of spaces is secured.

ARCHITECT'S SCALE

Scales are used to draw objects full size and either larger or smaller than full size. The architect's scale is available in either a flat shape or the triangular shape of boxwood. You must learn to use the scale well, since it is the basic measuring instrument for drawing. Notice that the architect's scale is made longer than 12″ so that the ends of the rule and the scales will not be damaged in use. Fig. 8-4. One edge of the scale is a rule with inches divided into sixteenths. This is stamped "16" at one end. If you wish to draw an object *full size* or *half size*, this rule must be used. For example, if

you are making a drawing half size (6″ = 1′), every one of the smallest divisions on the rule represents ⅛″ (instead of ¹⁄₁₆″) and each inch mark is 2″.

If the drawing must be made smaller than half size, this tool has other scales on it you can use. Remember in using any scale that you must think in terms of full-size dimensions, since they are always given that way on the completed drawing. For example, if you wish to make an object one-fourth full size (3″ = 1′), turn to the scale which has "3" stamped on the end. Notice that from zero to the end stamped "3", there are many small divisions. This distance represents 12″, or one foot. There are 12 larger divisions, each representing an inch. Every third inch mark is stamped 3, 6, and 9. Fig. 8-5. The smallest division that can be read directly on this scale is ⅛″. From zero to the other end there are long open divisions, each

8-3. Using dividers to lay off equal spaces. Notice how the dividers are rotated, from one point to another.

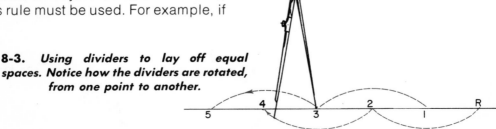

8-4. *An architect's scale.*

8-5. *This drawing of the scale 3″ equals 1′ shows a measurement of 10½″. Can you read it?*

representing 12″, or one foot. If you wish to lay off a measurement of 19″ on this scale, start at the large division mark stamped "1" to the left of the zero mark. Then go to the right of the zero to the largest division past 6, which is 7″. This would then be 19″. Once you get used to this scale it will be as easy to use as an ordinary rule.

On the opposite end of the tool is a scale stamped "1½″", or one-eighth size (1½″ = 1′). The smallest readable division on this scale is ¼″. Fig. 8-6.

For drawings of rooms, buildings, and house plans, a scale of ¼″ = 1′, or *quarter scale*, is often used. Remember, this is different from *quarter size*, or 3″ = 1′. Fig. 8-7.

Scales can also be used to make drawings that are larger than full size. Suppose you wish to make the object

one and one-half times full size. Use the scale stamped "1½." Then each division can represent 1″. To find a measurement of 4½″, start at the large division to the right of the zero mark stamped "4" and go to the left of the zero mark to the line stamped "6".

MECHANICAL ENGINEER'S SCALE

The mechanical engineer's scale is divided into measuring units that are very similar to the architect's scale. The measuring edges are limited to drawings that will be ⅛, ¼, ½, and full size.

CIVIL ENGINEER'S SCALE

There are several other kinds of scales that can be used in drafting. One that is good for drawing machine parts that are dimensioned in deci-

8-6. *This drawing of the scale 1½″ equals 1′ shows a reading of 17″, or 1 foot plus 5 inches.*

8-7. *This shows a part of the scale ¼″ equals 1′, showing measurement of 33″, or 2 feet and 9 inches.*

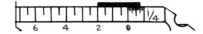

mals is called the civil engineer's scale. This has scale graduations of 10, 20, 30, 40, 50, and 60 parts to the inch. If you were making a full-size drawing of a machine part you would use the scale marked 10. Fig. 8-8. On this scale the distance between 0 and 1 is one full inch. This distance is divided into 10 equal parts (instead of 16 as on an ordinary rule); so each part represents 0.100 of an inch. Then, if the measurement is 3.250 (3¹/₄″), you will mark off 3 full inches and 2¹/₂ divisions beyond the 3″ mark. If the drawing is half size, the scale with 20 parts to the inch, or 10 parts to the half inch, should be used. On this scale the distance between 0 and 1 is

¹/₂″ and this distance is divided into 10 equal parts. The other scales are similar.

This scale is also used by people who draw maps (civil engineers and drafters in map making). The units on the scale may be used to represent feet, rods, or miles.

METRIC SCALES

The special scales for metric drawings are used like any other scale. There are a number of different kinds; three of the more common ones are shown in Fig. 8-9. The 1:1 scale (one mm = one mm) is used to make full-size drawings. For plans, elevations, and sections, use the 1:25, 1:50, or

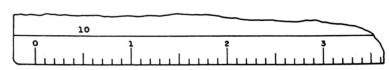

8-8. *A part of the civil engineer's scale. Notice the inches are divided into 10 equal parts.*

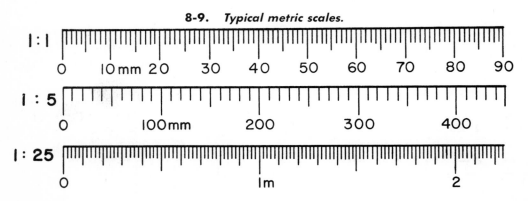

8-9. *Typical metric scales.*

	Metric Scale	Equivalent Scale (approx.) in Customary Units	Use
1:1	(1 mm = 1 mm)	1″ = 1″	full-size drawings
1:2	(1 mm = 2 mm)	1″ = 2″	half-size drawings
1:10	(1 mm = 10 mm)	1″ = 1′	one-tenth size drawings (approx.), details
1:25	(1 mm = 25 mm)	$\frac{1}{2}$″ = 1′	plans, elevations, sections
1:50	(1 mm = 50 mm)	$\frac{1}{4}$″ = 1′	″
1:100	(1 mm = 100 mm)	$\frac{1}{8}$″ = 1′	″
1:2500	(1 mm = 2500 mm)	25″ = 1 mile	maps

8-10. *Metric scales.*

1:100 scales. Detail drawings are made with the 1:10 scale. Fig. 8-10 shows metric scales which you will use in your drawings.

DRAFTER'S PENCIL SHARPENER AND POINTER

A pencil sharpener used by drafters removes the wood around the lead the correct distance but leaves the lead unsharpened. A pencil pointer, Fig. 8-11, can be used to sharpen the point to a cone shape and keep it that way. The point is inserted in the

8-11. *A pencil pointer used to sharpen the pencil lead after the wood has been removed on a draftsman's pencil sharpener.*

hold and the pencil rotated. Mechanical pencils can also be sharpened with this tool. A mechanical pencil is one in which the lead is held in a slip-chuck. Fig. 8-12.

TEMPLATES

Templates are plastic devices made with different shaped cutouts. Fig. 8-13. One, for example, may have holes of different sizes. Another may have the symbols used in electricity; still another, the symbols used in chemistry. These are a great help to people who are drawing in a particular field. You may find all types of templates in any complete catalog on drawing equipment.

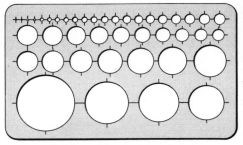

8-13. *Plastic templates.*

DRAFTING MACHINE

Many drafters use a drafting machine. This eliminates the need for a T square, triangle, and protractor. The two scales that are at right angles to each other can be adjusted by means of the protractor head to any angle for drawing inclined or slanted lines. Fig. 8-14.

8-12. *A mechanical drafting pencil.*

8-14. *A typical drafting machine setup.*

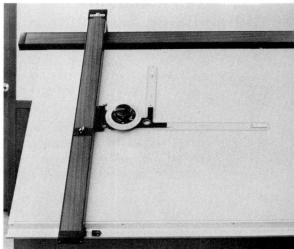

Unit 9. Making a Shop Sketch

In your workshop you will need a simple drawing of each project you are going to build. These simple drawings, sometimes called shop sketches, are made on squared paper. They will be used mostly by you yourself as you work in the shop. If several people are going to use it, this sketch should be made into a mechanical drawing. *Shop sketches are easier to make than freehand sketches.* This is true because it is

9-1. *Squared, or cross-section, paper usually has four or eight squares to the inch with an extra heavy line outlining the inches.*

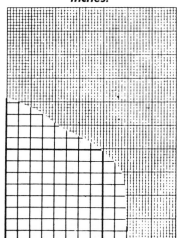

hard to judge size and proportion when sketching on plain paper. The only materials and tools you need are those listed here.

1. Materials: Squared or cross-sectioned paper. This paper is lined in squares, usually 4 or 8 to the inch. Fig. 9-1 shows an example. These squares help you to find the size of the object and to keep your lines straight. Sometimes paper with dots spaced $1/4''$ apart is used.

2. Tools: A medium soft H or HB pencil, an eraser, a 12-inch rule or straightedge, and a pencil compass (if desired). The compass may be used for drawing circles and arcs. These can be sketched freehand, however.

MAKING A SHOP SKETCH

1. Obtain a piece of cross-section paper.

2. Decide on the views you need to build the project. Often one view of each part is all that is needed.

3. Determine the scale. Decide if you can make the drawing full size, half size, or some other scale. If there are 8 squares to the inch, each square can represent $1/8''$, $1/4''$, $1/2''$, or any other fraction. For example, suppose you want to make a shop sketch

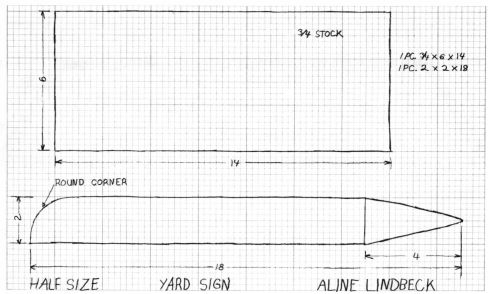

3/4 STOCK

1 PC. 3/4 × 6 × 14
1 PC. 2 × 2 × 18

6

14

ROUND CORNER

2

18

4

HALF SIZE　　　YARD SIGN　　　ALINE LINDBECK

9-2. *A simple shop sketch of a yard sign. As shown here, the scale is half size.*

of this yard sign. Fig. 9-2. Note that the post is 18″ long and the board is 14″. If it is drawn half size, both parts of the sign will go easily on 8½″ × 11″ paper. On paper with 8 squares to the inch, each square will represent ¼″.

4. Complete the drawing.

a. Draw the post. The post is 2″ square and 18″ long. Start about 1½″ up from the bottom of the page and in from the left edge about 1″. Mark a point. Draw a light horizontal line that represents the overall length of the post, or 9″. Draw a light vertical line for the thickness, 1″. Complete the rectangle. Measure in 2½″ from the right and measure up ½″ from the lower right corner. Draw the point at the end of the post. Round off the opposite corner either freehand or with a compass. Darken in the outline. Draw the extension and dimension lines, as shown in Fig. 9-2.

b. Make a one-view drawing of the board in the same general way.

c. Add the dimensions and notes. Notice that the lines and lettering aren't as perfect as you would make them in mechanical drawings. They are good enough for your own use, however. Remember this: to be useful the drawing or sketch must be correct. It doesn't have to be beautiful. It's a good drawing if you can build the project with it.

MAKING AN ISOMETRIC SHOP DRAWING

Another kind of paper is called isometric cross-section paper. It has lines drawn at angles of 30-60 degrees for making isometric drawings. Fig. 9-3. These are made in the same way as view drawings.

Note that the length of the sides of the isometric square is the same as that of the square formed by vertical and horizontal lines. This makes it possible to count the correct number of units along a vertical, horizontal, or slanted line, knowing that all will be equal. You should, therefore, start the isometric drawing at a point on the paper where the corners of both squares intersect.

Suppose you want to make an isometric drawing of this modern storage unit. Fig. 9-3. It is 16″ high, 12″ wide and 24″ long. It is necessary to use a scale of one-fourth size (3″ = 1′). Begin the drawing about two thirds of the distance over on the page. Draw a vertical line that is 4″ long (height). Draw a line at 30 degrees to the right that is 3″ long (width). Draw a line at 30 degrees to the left that is 6″ long (length). Complete the drawing as shown in Fig. 9-3, below.

Isometric cross-section paper eliminates the need for T square and triangles.

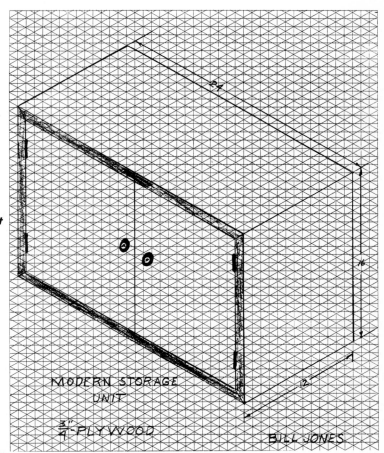

9-3. A storage unit drawn in isometric.

MODERN STORAGE
UNIT

¾″-PLYWOOD

BILL JONES

Unit 10. Doing Freehand Sketching

When Alexander Graham Bell got an idea for an early rocket airplane, he made a freehand sketch of the design. He then built the model and flew it. Just imagine, this rocket plane that flew was built from a simple sketch! Freehand sketching is a skill you can use every day of your life. There is always a piece of paper and a pencil handy. These are the only tools and materials you need to express your ideas on paper. For example, you might want to sketch a play in football or a project you'd like to build or a simple map showing a friend how to get to your house.

It's not easy to make good sketches. It takes a lot of practice. To sketch well you must be able to make neat lines, both straight and curved, freehand. You must also learn to judge distances to get proper proportion. With time and practice you can learn to sketch well.

TYPES OF LINES

The lines for freehand sketching are the same as those for mechanical drawing. *Construction* lines are used to "block in" an object. They show the location and approximate length of the permanent (object) lines. The *object* lines outline the shape of the part.

Hidden lines show edges and contours not visible to the eye. *Dimension* lines and *extension* lines show the sizes of the object, and the *center* line indicates the middle. Fig. 10-1. The outline and hidden lines are made quite heavy. The other lines are lighter. Make the construction lines so light that they do not need to be erased.

DRAWING STRAIGHT LINES

1. Use a piece of plain white typing paper. Have a sharp HB pencil and an eraser handy.

2. Hold the pencil loosely in your hand away from the point. Fig. 10-2. Pull the pencil along as you sketch. Don't push it.

3. To draw horizontal lines, place a point at the beginning and end of the line. You might try starting at one

10-1. *The lines in freehand sketching are the same as in mechanical drawing.*

Construction
object
Hidden

Dimension
Extension

Center

10-2. *The correct way to hold a pencil for sketching. Slowly draw a short, wiggly line. Exaggerate the wiggles at first.*

point and drawing short strokes as you move your hand along. Unless you are especially talented, do not try to draw a single straight line in one stroke because then your arm moves and the line becomes curved. Go over the series of short strokes to make the line solid. Practice this to see if you can draw a series of straight parallel lines.

4. To draw a vertical line, place a point at the upper and lower ends of the line. Line up the points with your eye as a carpenter does in sighting along the edge of a board. Draw the pencil toward you from the top to the bottom. (A second method is to move the paper so that all lines are drawn in a horizontal position.)

5. Draw slanted or inclined lines in the same way, following the directions shown by the arrow in Fig. 10-3.

SKETCHING SQUARES AND RECTANGLES

1. Draw light vertical and horizontal construction lines that intersect in the center. Fig. 10-4 (P. 60).

2. Mark points on these lines to show the approximate width and length of the object. You may measure from

the intersecting lines an equal number of spaces for drawing a square. Use your pencil in sketching as a measure or judging tool. For example, suppose the rectangle is twice as long as it is wide. Place your fingers on your pencil a distance from the point equal to the width of the rectangle. Turn the pencil sideways and twice that amount is the length. Fig. 10-5.

Draw light vertical and horizontal lines to form the square or rectangle. Fig. 10-4. Go over the lines to darken them. Do not erase the construction lines.

10-3. *The way to sketch lines. The arrow shows the direction your pencil should follow.*

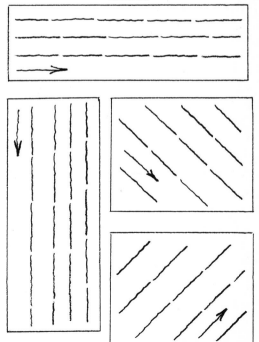

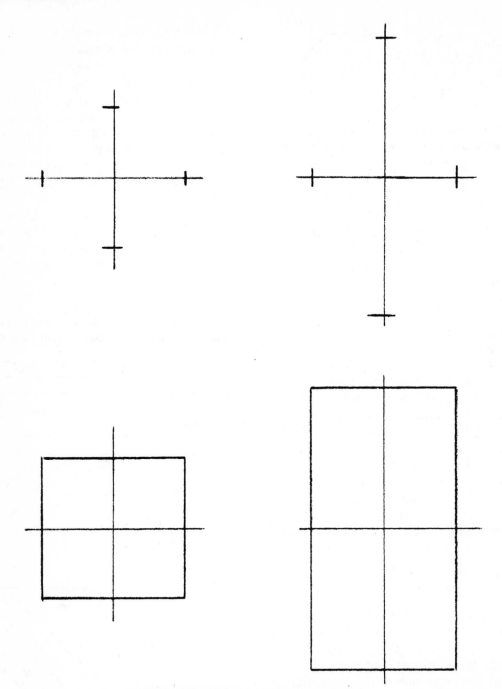

10-4. *Sketching a square or rectangle.*

SKETCHING TRIANGLES

1. Sketch light vertical and horizontal lines that intersect at one corner. Mark off one leg of the triangle along a vertical line and another leg along the horizontal line. Judge distances with your pencil.

2. Draw in the heavy vertical, horizontal and slanted lines to complete the triangle. Fig. 10-6.

3. An equilateral triangle should be sketched as shown in Fig. 10-7.

SKETCHING CIRCLES AND ARCS

A circle is the most difficult shape to sketch. Most of your first circles will look pretty wobbly and lopsided.

1. Draw light vertical and horizontal lines that intersect in the middle. For an even, smooth circle, draw extra lines at 45 degrees that intersect at the center. Fig. 10-8 (P. 62).

2. Judge the radius of the circle on your pencil. Hold your fingers at the center and make a small dash on

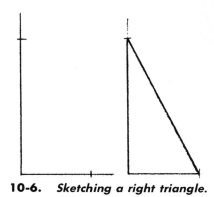

10-6. *Sketching a right triangle.*

each of the construction lines to outline the circle.

3. Join these marks with smooth, even curves to complete the circle.

4. Sketch an arc in the same general way. Fig. 10-9.

10-7. *Sketching an equilateral triangle.*

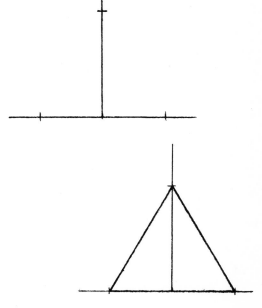

10-5. *Using a pencil as a guide in sketching. This will help you to get a good proportion.*

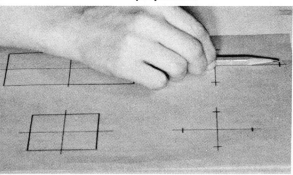

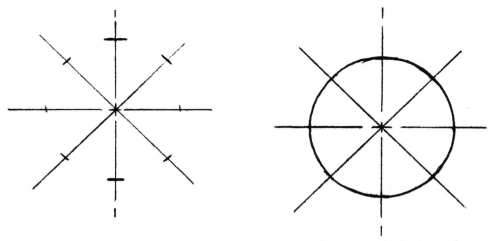

10-8. *Sketching a circle. Extra lines are sketched at 45 degrees to the horizontal to get a smooth curve.*

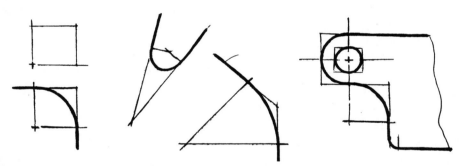

10-9. *Sketching curves and arcs by blocking in.*

MAKING A FREEHAND SKETCH

Most sketches that you will use in shopwork are view drawings. Follow the suggestions given previously in making the sketch. To make a sketch of the knife rack in Figs. 10-10 and 10-11, you would need a sketch of each part.

1. Sketch the back of the knife rack. Determine the approximate size or scale. The back is about 1½ times as long as it is wide. Make the sketch about *half size*.

2. Mark a point about 1″ in and 1″ (25 mm) up from the lower left-hand corner of the paper. Use this as a starting point for your sketch. Mark another point directly above it to represent the width of the back.

3. Using your pencil as a gauge, lay off a horizontal distance about 1½

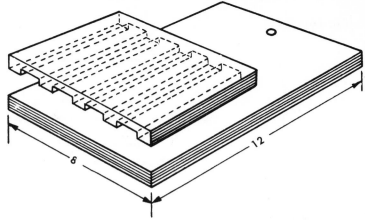

1 piece 8 × 12 × ³⁄₄

1 piece 8 × 6 × ³⁄₄

Ply Panel grade Interior fir plywood

Make knife slots by sawing ³⁄₈ **deep, rout out with chisel, width to fit your knives.**

10-10. *A perspective drawing of a simple knife rack.*

times this amount. Mark a point to show the end of the line.

4. Place another point above it to represent the other corner.

5. Sketch the light vertical and horizontal lines. Go over the lines to darken them. Decide on the size and location of the hole and sketch it.

6. You can sketch an end view if you want to. This is not necessary

10-11. *A photograph of the knife rack.*

though, since the thickness can be shown by a note.

7. Letter in the dimensions and any notes. Fig. 10-12 (P. 64).

8. Make a sketch of the front of the knife rack in a similar manner.

MAKING CABINET AND ISOMETRIC SKETCHES

Cabinet and isometric sketches are made in the same way as view sketches.

To make a cabinet sketch of a box or shelf, draw light vertical and horizontal lines to represent the front. Fig. 10-13. Then sketch inclined lines for the top and side. Along the inclined line judge a distance that is about half the true length. Go over these lines to outline the box or shelf. Fig. 10-14 shows a freehand sketch of a box.

Isometric sketches are made around three lines that are an equal distance apart. Judge distances along these lines and then sketch in the object. Figs. 10-15, 10-16, and 10-17 (P. 66).

63

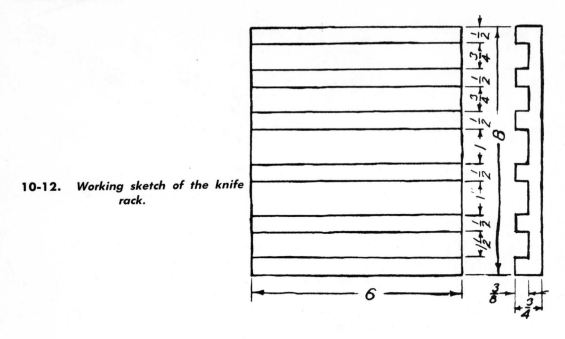

10-12. *Working sketch of the knife rack.*

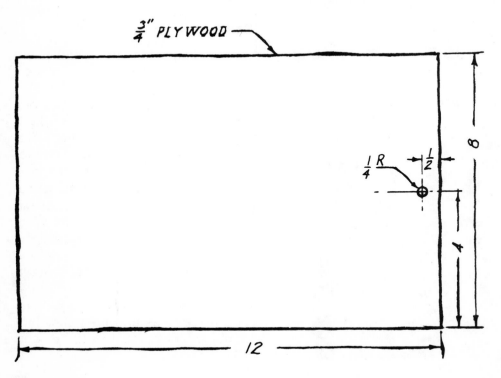

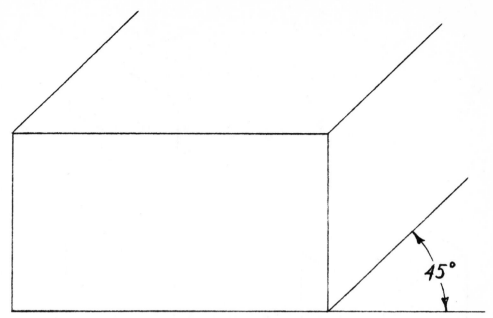

10-13. *Making a cabinet sketch.*

10-14. *Sketch of a box.*

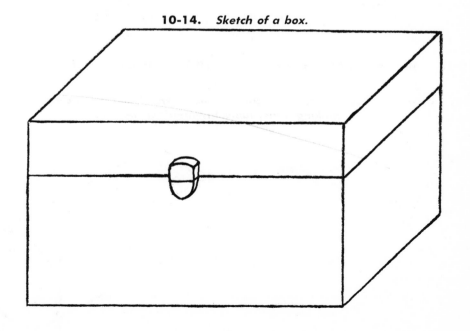

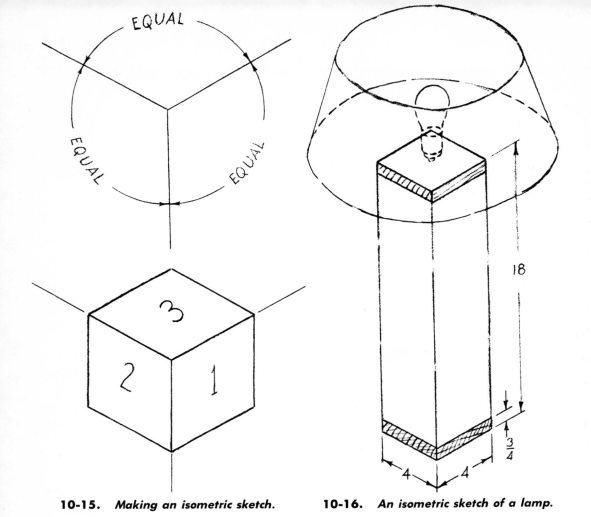

EQUAL EQUAL EQUAL

18

3
4

4   4

3
2   1

10-15. *Making an isometric sketch.*

10-16. *An isometric sketch of a lamp.*

10-17. *A cylinder. First, sketch an isometric box. Then, sketch the circle as you did in making a mechanical isometric circle.*

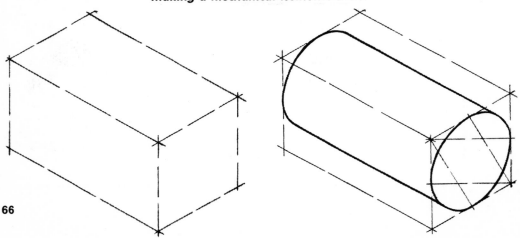

Unit 11. Making a Perspective Sketch

One of the most rewarding kinds of drawing activities is making perspective sketches. These are the most lifelike of all the drawings you can make. Fig. 11-1. They are not easy to make, but if you learn some simple methods and hints, you can do it. It also takes a lot of practice.

A SIMPLE PERSPECTIVE METHOD

The sketches in Fig. 11-2 (P. 68) show an easy way to construct a perspective sketch. Let's say that your problem is to sketch a long box.

The first step is to sketch the front and rear views on an angle of 45°. See Part A of Fig. 11-2. Next, darken in the lines on the lower left-hand quarter of the rear view, Part B. Finally, connect the corners of the two views, as shown in Part C. Go over all object lines to darken them. Do not erase any construction lines. (Remember, they should be very light anyhow). Cylinders, ovals, hexagons, and any other shape can be made the same way. Part D of Fig. 11-2. Practice making some other shapes. Soon you will be able to make a good sketch.

11-1. *Perspective, freehand sketches are attractive and lifelike.*

USING PERSPECTIVE GRID PAPERS OR TEMPLATES

Another good method of making perspective sketches is to use a plastic template that has guide lines. Fig. 11-3. These lines help you to get the proper slant wings. The guide lines on the template form an *angular* perspective. To use this method, place a thin piece of typing paper over the template and proceed as follows. (An airplane is used as an example.) Fig. 11-4.

1. The intersection of lines 1, 2, and 3 at point O determines the center of the airplane. All true dimensions are reduced by one-fifth for proper foreshortening in a perspective view. The distance between points O and P is half the length of the fuselage. Place half of the fuselage to the left of point O and the other half to the right of this point on line 1. Fig. 11-4.

2. Sketch the airplane wings with line 2 as a guide line. Center the left wing on line 2 with the wing attached to the fuselage at line 1. Make the right wing slightly shorter than the left wing. The wing trailing edge is parallel to line 2. Fig. 11-5.

3. Sketch the horizontal tail surfaces on line 4, with this line as a guide line. Sketch the right and left horizontal tail surfaces in the same manner as the wings. Remember to make the right one slightly shorter to take care of foreshortening. The horizontal tail surface trailing edge is located on line 4. Fig. 11-6.

4. Sketch the vertical tail surface. Notice how the guide lines automatically locate major parts in relation to one another. Add the details to complete the airplane sketch. Fig. 11-7.

A perspective sketching grid is shown in Fig. 11-8 (P. 70). To use,

11-2. *Steps in simple perspective sketching.*

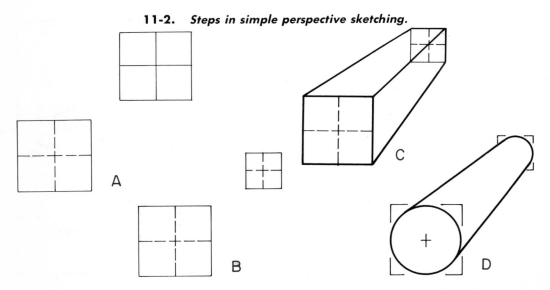

fasten a piece of tracing paper over the grid and sketch in the desired object. The guide lines will help you to sketch accurately.

SHADING PERSPECTIVE SKETCHES

Sketches can be made more realistic if you add shading to them. This helps you to see different parts of the sketch more clearly.

One method is to add lines, spaced to show darker or lighter areas. Fig. 11-9. Notice how some lines are made heavy and close together. These show dark shadows. Wide spaces show less shadow and more light. Water-color washes or colored pencils can also be used.

TECHNICAL ILLUSTRATIONS

Technical illustrations are pictorial drawings or retouched photographs showing products in different stages of development. These illustrations,

11-3. *Use a plastic template with thin paper over it as a guide in perspective sketching. The lines on the template help you to get the proper perspective.*

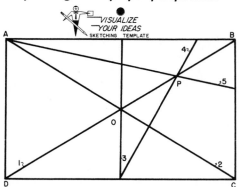

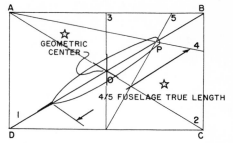

11-4. *Step 1 in sketching an airplane.*

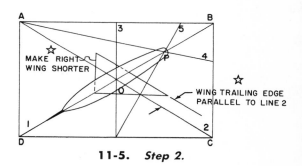

11-5. *Step 2.*

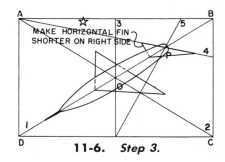

11-6. *Step 3.*

11-7. *Step 4.*

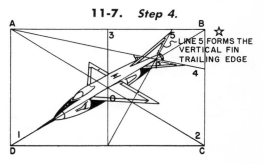

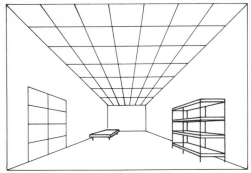

11-8. *A perspective grid.*

sketches, photographs, and diagrams are used to express ideas that cannot easily be put into writing.

Such illustrations are needed for showing a new product and for use during manufacturing. They are also used in booklets supplied to the buyer to show how to service, repair, or use a product. For example, a one-sheet assembly drawing might be sent with a wheelbarrow, while a large booklet of instructions might come with a lathe.

Unlike other drawings, most pictorial illustrations are done in ink.

TYPES OF TECHNICAL ILLUSTRATIONS

Technical illustrations can be any type—perspective, isometric, or oblique, for example. They may be exterior, interior, sectional, or phantom views. Here are some examples.

Cutaway Illustrations. Since they show the inside detail of an object, these are much like sectional views, except in picture form. Fig 11-10.

Exploded Pictorial. A good example of this is the tool post assembly on a metal lathe. The exploded pictorial shows the number needed to reorder parts and how the parts go together. Such drawings can be made either freehand or mechanically. Fig. 11-11.

Design Illustrations. Technical illustrators must be able to draw objects that do not yet exist, such as new types of spaceships. They must be able to imagine what these will look like and make suitable drawings.

11-9. *Line-shading perspective sketches.*

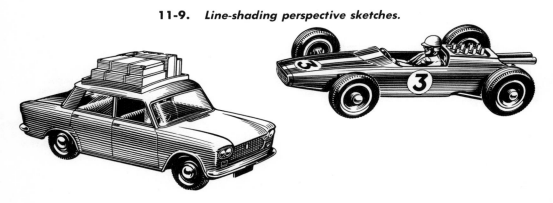

Peeled section showing
material build-up

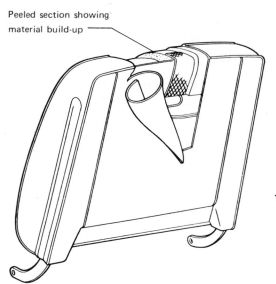

11-10. *Perspective cutaway sketch of an automobile seat.*

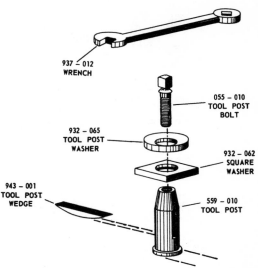

937 – 012
WRENCH

055 – 010
TOOL POST
BOLT

932 – 065
TOOL POST
WASHER

932 – 062
SQUARE
WASHER

943 – 001
TOOL POST
WEDGE

559 – 010
TOOL POST

11-11. *Exploded view of a tool-post assembly for a metal lathe. This illustrates how the parts go together.*

Unit 12. Learning to Letter

Lettering is really a kind of *freehand drawing* for forming the letters of the alphabet and numbers. Good lettering requires only patience and practice. You can learn to letter if you can make these four lines well: vertical, horizontal, slant, and curved. Fig. 12-1. This is because all letters are made up of these four lines in some combination. For example, an L is made with a single vertical line and a single horizontal line. The letter U is made with two vertical lines and a short curved line.

KINDS OF LETTERING

The lettering you will learn to do is called *single stroke Gothic.* That means it is a simple form of letters made with *single strokes* of the pencil. Look at an alphabet of capital letters. Notice that all letters are not

12-1. *Four practice strokes needed to learn to do good lettering. The arrows show the direction for making the lines.*

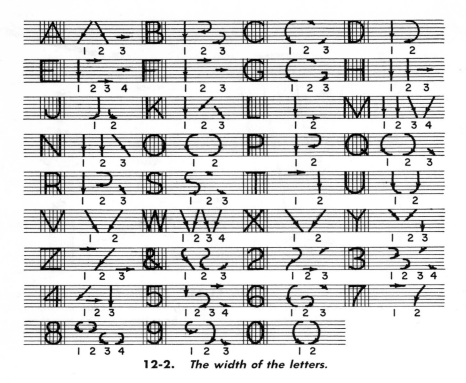

12-2. *The width of the letters.*

the same width. Imagine that a letter is to be made in a little box divided into six spaces wide and six spaces high. These would be the widths of some letters: C=5 spaces wide; M=6 spaces wide; I= only one space wide. Look at the width of the other letters. Fig. 12-2.

In beginning drawing, a simpler way is to make all the letters the same width except three. The J is a little narrower than the others, the I is just one line wide, and the W is a little wider than most. That's easier to remember.

Lettering that is done with all the letters at right angles to the horizontal is called *vertical* lettering. Lettering is also done with the letters forming an angle of about 67½ degrees to the horizontal. Fig. 12-3. This is called *inclined* lettering. Fig. 12-4.

Now let's look at the alphabet to see how the letters are drawn. Notice that E, F, H, I, L, and T combine vertical and horizontal lines only. The A, K, M, N, V, W, X, Y, and Z are made up of vertical, horizontal, and/or inclined lines. The remaining letters combine all these, plus the curve. Notice also, in Figs. 12-2, 12-3, 12-5, and 12-6, the arrows and numbers beside each letter. This suggests a way you can make each stroke to form

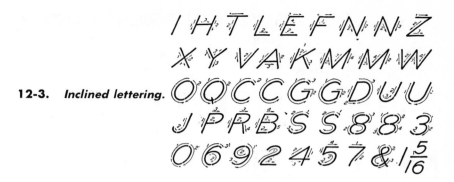

12-3. *Inclined lettering.*

the letters. Figs. 12-5 and 12-6 (Pp. 74 and 75) show both right- and left-handed people how to do this.

LETTERING PRACTICE

Now let's try to do some lettering. First, always use guidelines to keep the work straight. You should use a guideline even when you have a single dimension to put on a drawing so that the numbers look uniform in size. On most drawings letters are made about $\frac{1}{8}$" to $\frac{3}{16}$" (3 mm to 5 mm) high. The size, of course, varies with the over-all size of the drawing. It's easier to form smaller letters than larger ones. Lay out light, horizontal guidelines on your paper. These can remain on the drawing. Now select an H or 2H pencil for lettering. Be sure it is sharp. Sit or stand in a relaxed position. Hold the pencil lightly but firmly

in your hand. The reason many people never learn to do good lettering is that they tense up too much as they work the lines. Relax and take it easy. Rest your elbow on the drawing bench for firm, easy support.

Practicing Strokes. Try some vertical strokes, some horizontal strokes, some slant strokes, and some curved strokes. Fig. 12-1. Can you make these a uniform length, the lines straight, the curves smooth and always the same angle? After you have

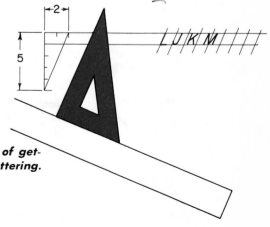

12-4. *A simple mechanical way of getting the correct angle for inclined lettering.*

• LETTERING WITH THE RIGHT HAND •

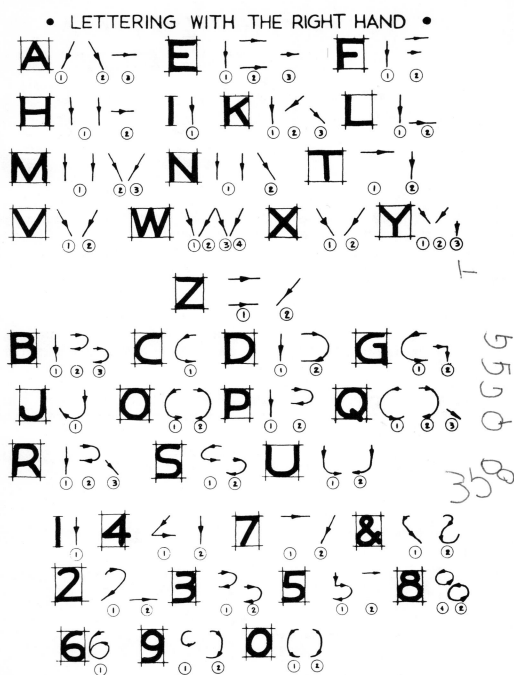

12-5. *The correct way to form the letters if you are right-handed.*

• LETTERING WITH THE LEFT HAND •

12-6. *The correct way of lettering if you are left-handed.*

done this exercise for a little while, begin to form the letters. The A has a horizontal line about one third of the way up. All the rest of the letters are divided about (but slightly above) center. The bottom of the letter should be a little larger than the top so it looks stable. Form all the *same shaped* letters at one time—that is, all the vertical and horizontal letters—and then go on to try others.

Making the O. Many of you will find that your poorest letters are those with curved lines. These are more difficult to make freehand. The O is the basic letter in this group. Make several of them until you get a feel for the circular motion. Don't be discouraged with your early lettering. It will not be as even as you'd like it to be. It takes practice.

Numbers. After doing capital letters, try numbers. These are made in the same general way. When lettering fractions, make the over-all fraction about two times the height of a whole number. For example, do it as in Figs. 12-7 and 12-8.

Words and Phrases. If spaced an equal distance apart, some letters appear farther apart than others. For example, an I that follows an L would appear much farther away than a D that follows an M. This is because the first two have a lot of white space around them and are *open* letters, and the other two have little or no space around them and are *closed* letters. Therefore, in forming words, place the open letters closer together than the closed letters. This will make the words appear to be uniformly spaced. Fig. 12-9.

FELT WASHER

LETTERS EQUALLY SPACED.
L & T APPEAR TOO FAR APART, H & E TOO CLOSE.

FELT WASHER

THIS LOOKS BETTER.
LETTERS APPEAR TO BE EQUALLY SPACED.

12-9. *The incorrect and correct spacing of letters to form words. Use your eye to judge the spacing.*

$3\frac{7}{8}$} TWICE THE HEIGHT OF THE WHOLE NUMBER

12-7. *The correct height of fractional numbers.*

12-8. *The correct method of drawing fractional numbers.*

$7\frac{5}{16}$ division line in line with center of whole number.
fractional numbers do not touch the line.

12-10. *The correct spacing to make sentences.*

MORE OR LESS THAN HEIGHT OF LETTERS
WIDTH OF AVERAGE LETTER
SELF CHECK YOUR LETTERING

AND LINE WORK. PRACTICE IS
$\frac{1}{4}$ WIDTH OF AVERAGE LETTER
TWICE HEIGHT OF LETTERS

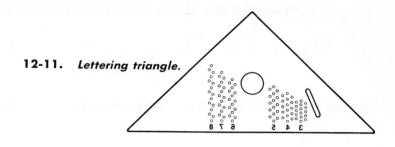

12-11. *Lettering triangle.*

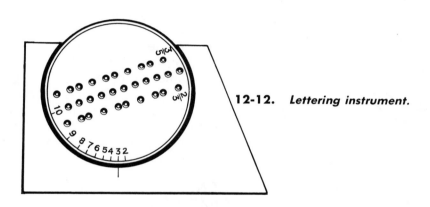

12-12. *Lettering instrument.*

When lettering a sentence, leave a space between words equal to the width of the average letter. The space between sentences should equal twice the height of the letters. The space between lines of words should be about equal to the height of the letters. Fig. 12-10.

LETTERING DEVICES

Two devices are commonly used for drawing guide lines and section lines. One is a lettering triangle with a series of countersunk holes. Fig. 12-11. The holes are planned in series for capital and lower-case letters. For example, to draw 1/8″ guide lines, use the hole marked 4 (the numbers show the spacing in 32nds). The long slender hole in the triangle edge is used to draw inclined guide lines at an angle of 67½ degrees. To use the triangle, place it on the upper edge of the T square. Place the pencil in the hole and then slide the triangle along to form the line. A lettering instrument is also used for drawing guide lines and section lines. Fig. 12-12. The correct space can be obtained by turning the plastic disc in the frame to the correct number (given in 32nds of an inch).

Unit 13. Dimensioning a Drawing

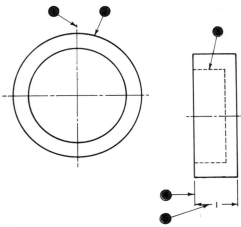

13-1. *Different kinds of lines: 1. Center line. 2. Object, or outline, line. 3. Invisible, or hidden, line. 4. Extension line. 5. Dimension line.*

13-2. *The three kinds of dimensions: detail, location, and over-all.*

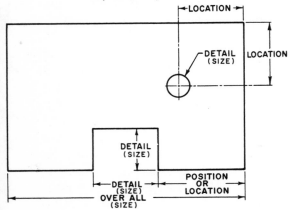

To be completely useful, a drawing must show the shape of the object, its size, and other information necessary to construct it. Even the simplest dimensions help to describe an object. The shape is shown by lines. Fig. 13-1. Dimensions tell the size or the measurements. Other information about the kind of material to use, number of pieces, and the like is added in the *title block* or *record strip* or is put on as a *note*.

GENERAL RULES FOR DIMENSIONING

1. Place the dimensions so they are easy and convenient to read.

2. Show only the measurements you need to build the object, nothing more. *These rules (1 and 2) are the most important to follow in all drawing.*

3. Do not duplicate or repeat dimensions. This just clutters up the drawing.

4. Use these three (some drafters say two—*size* and *location*) kinds of dimensions (Fig. 13-2).

a. Over-all (size) dimensions that show the total height, width, and length of the object.

b. Detail (size) dimensions that show the measurement of important

78

details. The *diameter of a hole* is a good example.

c. Location, or position, dimensions that show where the details are.

5. Place the dimensions on the drawing in one of two ways. Both are correct and either can be used for all kinds of drawings. However, be uniform in each drawing. In the more modern method first used by aircraft companies, the dimensions are placed so they are read only from the *bottom*. Fig. 13-3A. The traditional or regular method is to place dimensions so they are read from the *bottom and right side*. Fig. 13-3B.

6. Letter the dimensions correctly. Most dimensions on beginning draw-

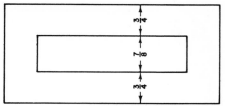

13-4. *Notice that it's easier to read these dimensions when they are placed inside the drawing. If possible, however, keep the dimensions off the view.*

ings are shown in *inches and fractions* of an inch. On many drawings used in industry, the dimensions are given in *decimals*. For example, instead of 1¹/₄″, the dimension is shown as 1.250″. Metric dimensions will also be used.

WHERE AND HOW TO DIMENSION

1. Place all dimensions *outside* the views rather than right on the drawing. If possible keep them all *between* the views. If easier to read, however, certain dimensions can be placed inside the views. Fig. 13-4. (A "view" is the part of a thing shown by the drawing—front, top, or side, for instance.)

2. Place the dimensions on the view which shows the shape the clearest. Do not put them on other views where they are not needed. Fig. 13-5 (P. 80). Usually the height and length are placed on the *front view*.

3. The *extension lines* should be light, sharp lines starting about ¹/₁₆″ away from the outline or object. Fig. 13-1. They should extend only slightly

13-3. *The two methods of placing dimensions. (A) The one direction (unidirectional) method of dimensioning—all figures made straight up and down. (B) The two direction (aligned) system of dimensioning—read from the bottom and right-hand edge of the paper. You have to turn the drawing to read side figures.*

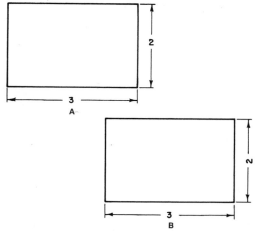

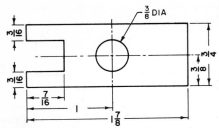

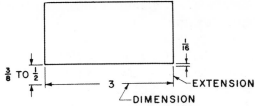

13-5. *Dimensions placed on a drawing where they are easiest to read. Notice how the dimensions are "staggered" and that the extension lines do not cross the dimension lines. For example, the 1⁷/₈ dimension is placed below smaller dimensions and is connected with added extension lines, so that none of the lines cross. Your instructor can help make this clear. See Fig. 13-1.*

13-6. *The correct postion for extension and dimension lines.*

beyond the arrowheads of the outside dimension lines. Fig. 13-6.

4. The dimension lines should start about ³/₈″ to ¹/₂″ from the outline or object. If there are several parallel dimension lines they should be ¹/₄″ to ³/₈″ apart. Fig. 13-6.

5. If there are several parallel dimension lines, don't place dimension *figures* above each other; "staggering" them makes them easier to read. Fig. 13-5.

6. Always place the detail and

location dimensions inside the over-all dimensions. Fig. 13-7.

7. Always show each over-all (long size) dimension only once on the drawing. Don't repeat dimensions.

8. Never allow dimension lines to cross extension lines.

9. Never use a center line as a dimension line. (Center lines may cross all other lines because they are lighter and are "broken" lines.)

10. Use *inches* to and including 72, and *feet and inches* above this amount. Use the mark ″ for inches and use ′ for feet. If all dimensions are in inches, *the inch mark can be omitted.*

11. Avoid bringing an extension line from an invisible or hidden line (which shows a part of an object

13-7. *Notice that the detail (short size) dimensions are placed inside the over-all (long size) dimension. *This dimension is usually omitted on machine drawings where great accuracy is required. It can be added and marked REF. (Reference). This dimension is included on house plans and other construction drawings or on any drawing where great accuracy is not required.*

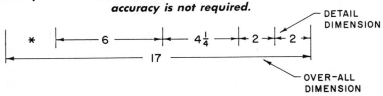

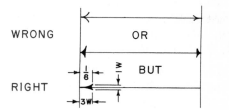

13-8. *In this view some dimensions are shown from invisible lines. This should be done only if it helps to make the drawing of the visible surface easier to read.*

behind the surface). In some cases, especially on the side view, it may be necessary. Fig. 13-8.

12. If the space for dimensioning is small, place the arrowheads *outside* the extension lines, pointing in, as shown in Fig. 13-9.

13. If the drawing is symmetrical (equal on both sides) only *half* the view is needed. The symbol ₵ on the center line is then used. Fig. 13-10.

DRAWING ARROWHEADS

Arrowheads are drawn on one or both ends of most dimension lines. Only one arrowhead is used on the

dimension line for the *radius*. The arrowhead should be about three times as long as it is wide. For the average drawing it should be about $1/8''$ long. Examples of correct and incorrect ways to draw arrowheads are shown in Fig. 13-11.

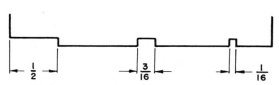

13-9. *Methods of dimensioning small spaces.*

13-11. *Correct and incorrect arrowheads.*

13-10. *Only half a view is needed for an object that is symmetrical (the same on both sides).*

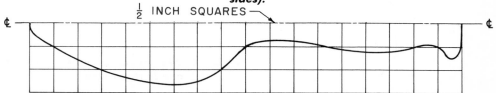

$\frac{1}{2}$ INCH SQUARES

DIMENSIONING CIRCLES, ARCS, AND ANGLES

1. Always dimension the *diameter* of circles, cylinders, and holes. Fig. 13-12. There are three common ways:

a. The dimension may be placed *inside the circle.* Avoid placing the dimension too close to the center lines.

b. The dimension can be placed *outside the circle,* with the dimension line either vertical or horizontal.

c. *Leaders* can be used. These are fine lines drawn at a 45- or 60-degree angle to the center, just touching the circumference. An arrowhead is drawn on one end and a short horizontal line on the other. Leaders can also be used to add notes to a drawing.

2. Place DIA after the dimension, if it is not clear that it is a circle or hole. DIA means "diameter."

3. Where there are several equal size holes around a circle, indicate the size of the hole and the number. Fig. 13-13. If they are not spaced equally apart, show the location of the holes by lettering in the *angle* between the holes.

4. Give the *radius* of an arc. Place an R after the dimension. Follow one of the methods shown in Fig. 13-14,

according to how big the space you have for the dimension.

5. Place dimensions for angles so they can be read without turning the paper. Fig. 13-15.

ADDING NOTES TO DRAWINGS

Notes are placed on the drawing to give the worker additional information not shown by the dimensions.

Here is some typical information that might be added to a drawing:

1. In a one-view drawing, the thickness and kind of material.

2. Information about the kind of material to use.

3. A special process that must be completed, such as hardening, annealing, tempering, or twisting.

4. A special dimension that may vary depending on the use of the drawing. For example, a clock frame may have the note "drill to fit clock," thus showing the diameter of the opening.

5. A dimension not shown on a two-view drawing. For example, on a two-view drawing of a book case there might be the note "back—1/4" plywood."

6. A special kind of finish to be applied.

7. Several holes of the same size could be indicated with a note, "all holes 1/4"."

13-12. *Circles should be dimensioned in one of these ways.*

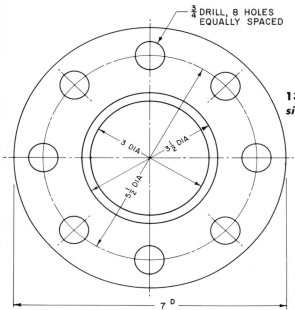

13-13. *The correct method of dimensioning an object in which there are several equally spaced holes.*

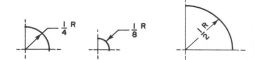

13-14. *Dimensioning an arc. Use any one of the methods shown.*

8. On a casting the note might be added, "all fillets and rounds 1/4R."

9. Any other information not given in the dimensions or in the title block or strip that would be useful to the person using the drawing.

The notes are placed on the drawing in a convenient and easy-to-read location. On the average drawing they are lettered in 1/8" capitals.

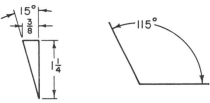

13-15. *Dimensioning an angle.*

DUAL DIMENSIONING

Dual dimensioning means placing two sets of sizes on a drawing, both metric and customary. This was explained in Unit 3. One kind of dual dimensioning is shown in Fig. 3-8. There are two other types in use today. In one type, a letter is used in place of the dimension. Fig. 13-16 (P.

84). To find the metric and customary sizes, the reader studies the chart placed on the drawing. This is a good method because the drawing is not cluttered with two sets of dimensions. In the other type, Fig. 13-17, only the metric dimensions are shown. The reader finds the customary sizes by studying a special chart which shows metric and customary equivalents. This chart shows how many inches equal a certain number of millimetres.

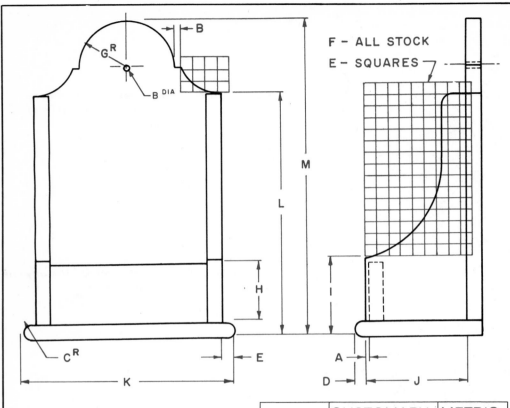

F — ALL STOCK
E — SQUARES

13-16. *Letters are used in place of sizes on this example of dual dimensioning. Study the chart to get both the metric and customary sizes.*

LETTER	CUSTOMARY in inches	METRIC in mm
A	$1/8$	3
B	$1/4$	6.5
C	$5/16$	8
D	$3/8$	9.5
E	$1/2$	12.5
F	$5/8$	16
G	2	51
H	$2 5/8$	68
I	$2 3/4$	70
J	$4 1/4$	108
K	$8 7/8$	225
L	$10 1/2$	267
M	$13 5/8$	346

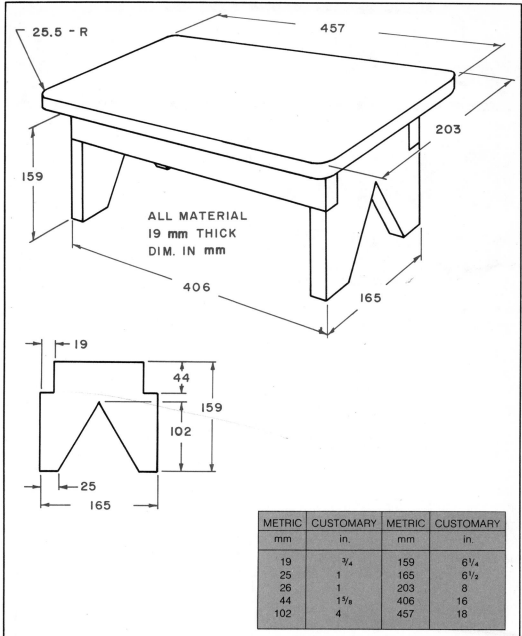

METRIC	CUSTOMARY	METRIC	CUSTOMARY
mm	in.	mm	in.
19	3/4	159	6¼
25	1	165	6½
26	1	203	8
44	1⅝	406	16
102	4	457	18

13-17. *In this example of dual dimensioning, only the metric sizes are shown. To find the customary sizes, study the equivalency chart.*

Unit 14. Completing a One-View (Layout) Drawing

14-1. *Some art-metal objects, such as this key tag, need only a one-view drawing.*

Many of the drawings that you make and use in the lab and in everyday life need only one view. For example, only one view is needed as a layout for a ball field, the design for bookends, or a pattern. Figs. 14-1 and 14-2. Drawings in electricity, home planning, and weaving also require only one view. Here is the way to make a one-view drawing. Fig. 14-3. You will find that other drawings are made in about the same way.

1. Draw a border on the sheet. A border is placed on a drawing to improve its appearance. It's like putting a frame on a picture. Then, too, the border says, "Everything inside these lines is important. Be sure to study it carefully." The small area

beyond the border can be used to bind several drawings together. To lay out a border proceed as follows:

a. Choose a piece of $8\frac{1}{2}'' \times 11''$ paper. Locate the paper on the drawing board in a horizontal position. Hold the rule against the upper edge of the T square. Measure in $\frac{1}{4}''$ from the left edge of the paper. Make a dot or small dash. Then, $10\frac{1}{2}''$ from this mark, place another small dot.

b. Draw two light vertical *construction* lines the total height of the paper. These are very light lines which show the location and approximate length of the permanent lines. Use a 3H or 4H pencil or press very lightly with your 2H pencil.

c. Hold the rule against a triangle in a vertical position. Measure up $\frac{1}{4}''$ from the bottom of the paper. From this point measure $8''$ and make a second dot or mark.

14-2. *A one-view drawing of the key tag shown in Fig. 14-1.*

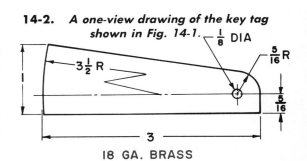

18 GA. BRASS

d. Draw two light horizontal lines to form the border. Don't worry if the corners cross.

2. Draw a title block or record strip. Certain information about what the drawing is and who made it must be given on each drawing. This is placed in the *title block* or *record strip.* School drawings usually give the name and location of the school, the name of the object, the scale, the student's name, and the number of

the drawing. Often there is a place for the instructor to okay the work.

The title block or strip can be drawn in the lower right-hand corner, along the bottom, or along the right side. Let's place this title block across the bottom. Measure up from the border line ⁵/₈" and draw a heavy line across the paper. Divide this space into five equal parts vertically. Draw five light guide lines across the page. Divide the area horizontally into three parts

14-3. *A complete one-view drawing of a cheese-cutting board. The title block, or record strip, at the bottom, is ⁵/₈" wide.*

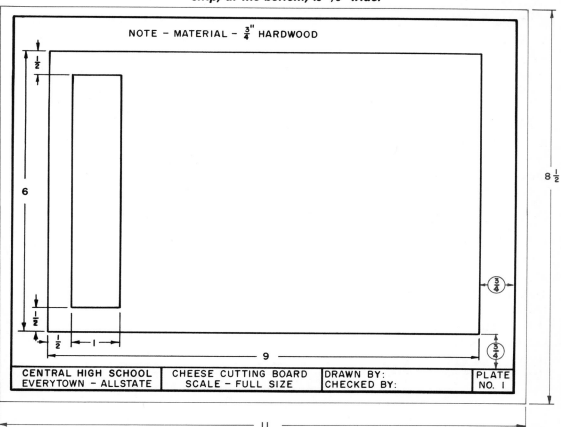

3¼" wide and one part ¾" wide. The title block or strip may be drawn in several other different ways. Fig 14-4.

3. Center the drawing. All drawings are centered on the paper to improve the appearance of the finished drawing. To center the cheeseboard, proceed as follows:

a. Measure the length of the board (9"). Subtract this from the horizontal distance inside the border lines (10½"). Divide this amount (1½") in half. Measure in from the left edge this distance (¾") and draw a light vertical line.

b. Measure the width of the board (6"). Subtract this from the vertical distance between the upper border line and the title strip (7⅜"). Divide this amount (1⅜") in half. To make the drawing appear on center use ¾" instead of ¹¹/₁₆". Measure up from the border line a distance of ¾" and draw a light horizontal line. These are the two reference lines from which all other measurements are made.

4. Complete the layout. Lay out a distance of 9" along the horizontal line and 6" along the vertical line. Draw these two light construction lines to "block in" the over-all size. Measure a distance of ½" from the left edge of the object. Draw a light vertical line. Measure a distance of 1" from that line, and draw a second vertical line. Now measure ½" from the top 9" line and from the bottom 9" line. Draw two horizontal lines to connect the two vertical lines you drew earlier. You now have the outline of the board, plus the rectangular opening.

Darken the straight lines to complete the view, using an H or 2H pencil. These are called *object* or *visible* lines. Use an H or HB pencil to darken the border lines. Form sharp corners that do not overlap. Erase the construction lines beyond the corners. The *border* lines should be the heaviest on the page. These lines are usually darkened in last so they won't

14-4. *Another simple title block, or record strip, to use on 8½" × 11" paper. Note the difference between this one and that shown in Fig. 14-3.*

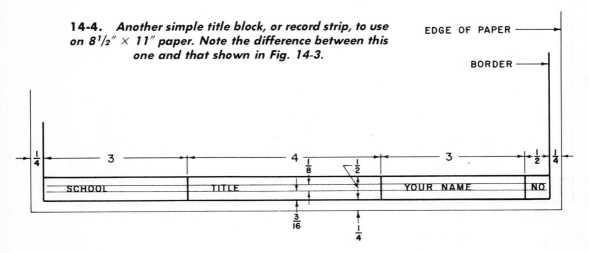

smudge as you work on the drawing. Erase the construction lines beyond the object or outline lines.

You can also do layout work using the metric scale. Remember to use mm instead of cm because the mm will be used more in drafting.

5. Dimension the drawing. The drawing must give dimensions, or sizes, so that the object can be made in the lab. Draw the extension and dimension lines.

6. Letter in the dimensions and information in the title block. Place the dimensions so they can be read from the bottom and the right side. Letter in the necessary information in the title block or record strip. Add the note on the drawing which tells the kind and thickness of wood to use.

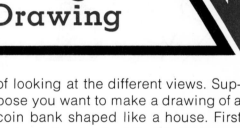

Unit 15. Making a Working Drawing

Working drawings are made for building or constructing an object. The drawing must show the exact shape and size. This can best be done by making a drawing of two, three, or more views. This is called a *working drawing* because it is used to "work from" when making anything. It is also called a *multiview drawing* because it shows the several views. Still another name is *orthographic projection*, which means "right-writing," or that the views are at right angles to each other.

UNDERSTANDING WORKING DRAWINGS

There are two easy ways to understand how a working drawing is made. One method is the *natural way*

of looking at the different views. Suppose you want to make a drawing of a coin bank shaped like a house. First look at the front of it. What do you see? You see the outline of the front view showing the *height* and *length*. Fig. 15-1 (P. 90). When you look down on the house, you see the top view, which shows the *width* and *length*. Fig. 15-2. When you look at the right side, you see the right side, or end, view. You see the *height* and *width*. Fig. 15-3. Each view shows the true size, shape, and other details of that part of the house. The three views when placed on a single piece of paper show how the object looks as a *working drawing*. Fig. 15-4.

A second way to understand working drawings is to imagine the object

15-1. *Look at the front of the coin bank, as this fellow is doing. This front view shows the height and length, as well as details of the front surface.*

15-2. *The top view shows the width and length, and details of the ridge, chimney, and gutters.*

15-3. *The right side, sometimes called the end view, shows the height and width, and side details—windows, etc.*

in a *clear plastic box.* Figs. 15-5 and 15-6. Notice how the box is hinged at the top and the right side of the front surface. This allows the box to be opened up. Sketch the front view on the front surface of the box. Fig. 15-7. Sketch the top view on the top surface. Fig. 15-8. Finally, sketch the right side view of the object on the right side of the box. Fig. 15-9. When

15-4. *This is the way the three views of the bank are placed on a paper, folded to show how the views are drawn.*

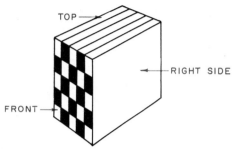

TOP

RIGHT SIDE

FRONT

15-5. *A pictorial drawing of a design block. Each of the three surfaces can be easily identified. Study these surfaces.*

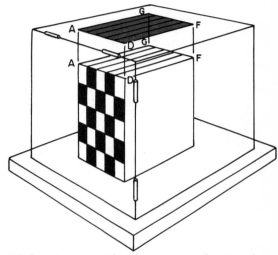

15-8. *Drawing the top view on the top of the box. The edge AD is the same as the edge AD on the front view.*

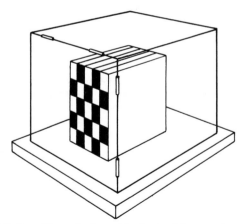

15-6. *The design block inside a clear plastic box. Notice the way the top and side of the box are hinged to the front.*

15-7. *Drawing the front view of the block on the front of the plastic box. The corners are marked A, B, C, and D.*

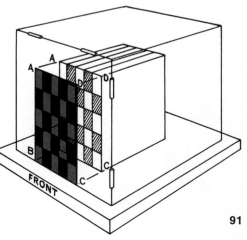

FRONT

15-9. *Drawing the right-side view on the right side of the box. Notice the edge DC is the same as the edge DC on the front view.*

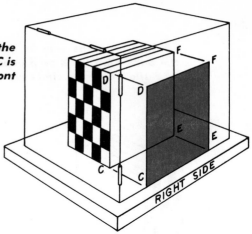

you open out the sides of the box, you will see the three views in their proper positions. Fig. 15-10. If you now remove the lines of the box itself, the working drawing will look like Fig. 15-11.

Most objects have *six sides*, namely, front, top, right side, left side, bottom and rear (back). For most drawings, only the front, top and right sides are shown.

In making a working drawing the views can be completed in part by *projection*, "making" one view by using the width, height or length of a complete view. In Fig. 15-12, the height of the front view can be "pro-

15-10. *Now the box is opened up and you can see the three views in the proper positions.*

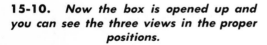

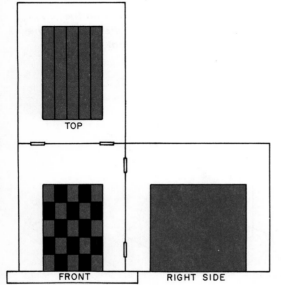

TOP

FRONT   RIGHT SIDE

15-11. *The plastic box is removed and you see the three-view drawing of the block.*

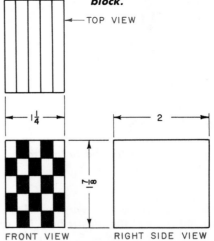

TOP VIEW

$1\frac{1}{4}$ 2

$1\frac{7}{8}$

FRONT VIEW   RIGHT SIDE VIEW

jected" to form the height of the side view. It is possible also to complete the side view by projection. First draw the front and top views. Then draw a light line at an angle of 45 degrees at the upper right-hand corner. Now project the *height* from the front view and the *width* from the top view as shown. Notice also how the width can be projected with a compass by

drawing light arcs from the top view to the side view.

THINGS TO REMEMBER ABOUT WORKING DRAWINGS

1. The front view (one of the principal views) should always be the best one or the one that shows the most distinct shape of the object.

2. Arrange the front view so that

15-12. *Notice the location of the five views and how the views can be projected one to the other. The height of the front view can be projected to the height of the right- or left-side view. The length can be projected from the front view to the top or bottom view. The width can be projected from the top view to the right- or left-side view by drawing arcs a-a", b-b". The width can be projected from the top to the right side by drawing a line at 45 degrees and then projecting a line from a to a' to a" and b to b' to b".*

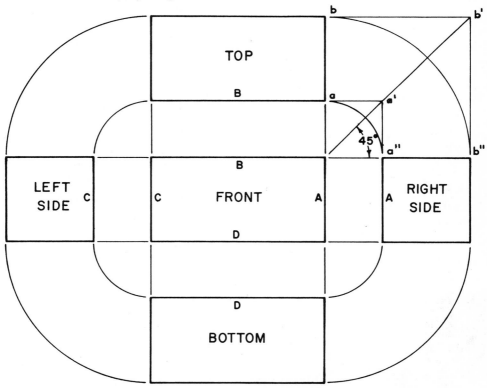

the other views will have the fewest number of hidden lines. See Unit 16.

3. Show only the number of views that you actually need. Sometimes you will need two, most often three and, in rare cases, four or more.

4. The *front view* is placed in the lower left-hand corner of the paper.

5. The *top view* is always placed in line with and directly above the *front view*.

6. The *right-side view* (*end view*) is in line with and directly to the right of the front view.

7. The height (sometimes called thickness) and the length of the object are shown in the *front view*.

8. The width (sometimes called the depth) and length of the object are shown in the *top view*.

9. The height (or thickness) and width (or depth) of the object are shown in the *right-side view*.

10. Center the whole drawing on the page.

11. Allow about ½″ to 1″ (12 to 25 mm) between views.

MAKING A THREE-VIEW DRAWING

Let's try to make a three-view drawing of an oilstone. Fig. 15-13.

15-13. *An oilstone is a simple rectangular shape. The arrow shows the side selected for the front view.*

1. Draw the border line and title block or record strip. See Unit 14.

2. Lay out the drawing inside the border so that it is well balanced. Remember that you have an area of $7\frac{3}{8}″ \times 10\frac{1}{2}″$ inside the *border lines* and *title block*. First determine the length (6″) and width (2″) of the object. Allow space between the views (1″). More than 1″ may be left between views if a great many dimensions are needed. Remember, however, that the distance between views must be equal. The total distance, then, horizontally, is 9″ (6″ + 2″ + 1″). This means that you should start ¾″ in from the left border line. The thickness of the oilstone is 1″ and the width 2″. With a distance of 1″ between views, there are $3\frac{3}{8}″$ remaining. The distance you should start up from the title block is thus $1\frac{3}{4}″$.

3. With your rule held against the triangle, make a short dash that will locate the horizontal lines of the views of the object.

4. With your rule held against the upper edge of the T square, make a short dash to locate the vertical lines.

5. Draw light horizontal and vertical lines to "block in" the object as shown in Fig. 15-14.

6. Retrace the outline of each view of the object with an H or 2H pencil. Erase the construction lines.

7. Draw in the dimension lines and extension lines.

8. Add the dimensions and notes.

9. Darken in the border line and letter the information in the title block or record strip. Fig. 15-15.

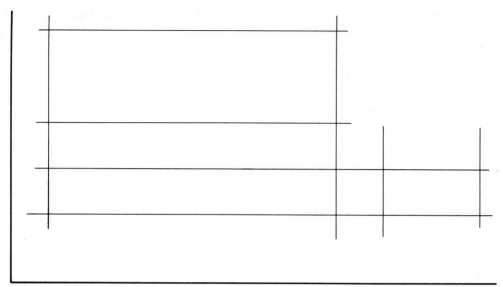

15-14. *Blocking in the three views with light construction lines. These lines should be made as light as possible. Don't worry about the corners being crossed. These can be erased after the drawing is completed.*

15-15. *The three-view drawing of the oilstone. The dimensions that are circled are there for your convenience. If you make the drawing, do not include these.*

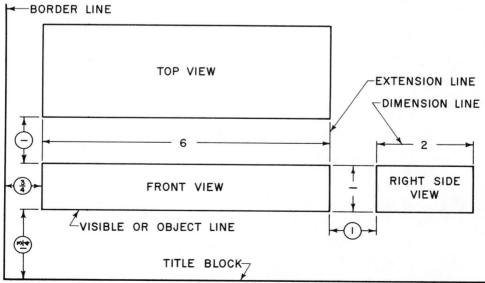

Unit 16. Drawing Views with Hidden Surfaces

If you removed the lead from the pencil you are using, there would be a hole through it. From the side of the pencil you couldn't see this hole, but you'd know it was there. In a working drawing this hole would be shown with *invisible* or *hidden* lines. These lines are used on all view drawings to show edges, holes, corners, and surfaces that cannot be seen from that view but are a part of the object.

USING INVISIBLE OR HIDDEN LINES

Fig. 16-1 shows a mirror frame with a rabbet edge into which the mirror will fit. Fig. 16-2 shows three views of the frame. Notice that from the front and top views there would be no invisible or hidden lines. On the side view, however, a hidden line is needed to show the inside corner of the rabbet.

The turned wooden bowl in Fig. 16-3 is illustrated with a pictorial sketch and a two-view working drawing. Invisible lines are needed in both views. Can you tell what part of the bowl each of these lines represents? A working drawing of a bookend is shown in Fig. 16-4. One hidden line is required on the front view. Why?

RULES TO FOLLOW FOR HIDDEN, OR INVISIBLE, LINES

1. Make the dashes of equal length (about 3 mm or approx. $1/8''$) with an equal amount of white space (1 mm or approx. $1/32''$) between.

16-1. *A mirror frame like this would have a rabbet edge around the back where the mirror fits.*

2. If two invisible lines are parallel to one another, see that the dashes are "staggered."

3. Invisible lines should always start and stop with one of the object or outline lines. Never start with a white space except when it is a continuation of a solid line.

4. When invisible lines join in a corner or cross each other, always cross or join the dashes, not the white space. Fig. 16-3.

5. The weight of the line should be somewhat lighter than the outline or object lines.

There are many industrial machines which contain hidden surfaces. The drafter must draw these carefully to show all these hidden parts.

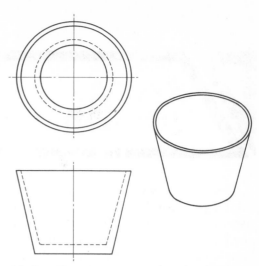

16-3. *Here is a pictorial and a two-view drawing of a turned bowl. Notice that in the corners on the side view the dashes forming the invisible lines join.*

16-4. *The three-view drawing of a book-end. The invisible line shows the thickness of the base on the front view.*

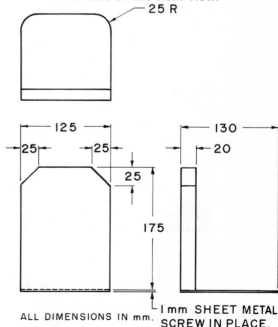

25 R

125
25   25
25
130
20
175

ALL DIMENSIONS IN mm.

1mm SHEET METAL
SCREW IN PLACE.

16-2. *To draw a three-view section of the frame, an invisible line is needed on the right-side view.*

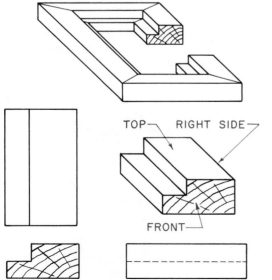

TOP   RIGHT SIDE

FRONT

Unit 17. Working Drawings with Two Views

What would a working drawing of a rolling pin look like? Fig. 17-1. If you used three views what would you see? Yes, the front view and the top view would be exactly alike. Often it is not necessary to have three views for a good working drawing. This is almost always true of cylindrical shapes. Fig. 17-2. Many other objects can be drawn to show all needed information with only two views.

POINTS TO REMEMBER

1. Always make the most distinctive view the front view. For example, suppose you are making a working drawing of the top of a footstool or small table. Fig. 17-3. You need only two views—one to show its shape and one to show the thickness. Fig. 17-4. Since the circular shape is the most important, this should be made the front view.

2. Draw a top or side view, whichever is best, as the second view. Fig. 17-4. Sometimes it is more convenient to use the top view and sometimes the side view is best.

3. Whenever possible use only two views even though three could be drawn. It is often a waste of effort and space to show the third view. This is especially true of woodworking drawings. For example, nothing new could be learned by making a side view of this small wall shelf. Fig. 17-5. All the information you need for making it is shown on the front and top views.

17-2. *A cookie jar like this would require only two views. With a note, only one would be necessary.*

17-1. *Two views of this rolling pin are alike. A two-view drawing, then, is all that is needed.*

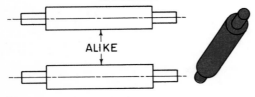

ALIKE

98

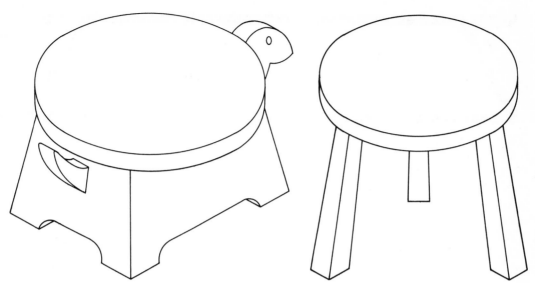

17-3. *The top of a table or footstool would require only two views.*

17-4. *Two methods of drawing the top of a table or stool.*

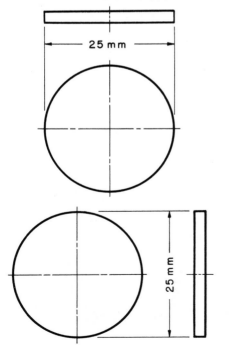

17-5. *Would anything be added by drawing a third view of this wall shelf?*

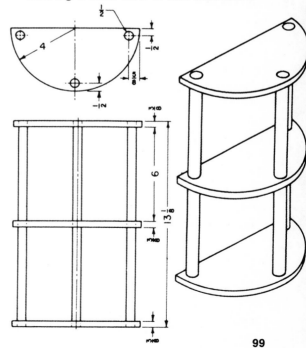

Unit 18. Making a Perspective Drawing

As you learned in Unit 2, pictorial drawings look much like the object they represent. In the next three units, you will read about three kinds of pictorial drawings: perspective, isometric, and oblique.

Drawing that looks most like a photograph is called *perspective* drawing. Perspective drawings are used by many different people. The architect makes a perspective of some new home or building he or she is designing.

Perspectives are often used for illustrations in newspapers and magazines. They can show what a future model car or plane looks like, for instance. Some industries use perspective drawings and sketches in construction. They are useful because the perspective shows the actual appearance and the drawing can be dimensioned with sizes.

Perspective drawings are made as the object appears to the eye. Note the photograph of the railroad tracks. Fig. 18-1. See how the tracks appear to come together at some distant point. This is called the *vanishing point* (V.P.). This point is on the *horizon*. Notice also that the things that are *below* eye level tend to move upward and get smaller toward the horizon. Objects *above* eye level, such as the telephone poles, tend to get shorter and move downward toward the horizon.

KINDS OF PERSPECTIVES

There are two kinds of perspective drawings—the *parallel* and the *angular*. Parallel perspective is seldom used. It has one vanishing point. Figs. 18-2 and 18-3.

18-1. *A photograph of a railroad track. Notice the vanishing point. What kind of perspective is it?*

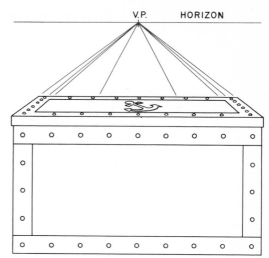

18-2. *Here is a sea chest that we'll use to illustrate perspective drawing.*

18-3. *A parallel perspective of the sea chest.*

About 90 percent of all perspectives are of the angular type. This has two vanishing points. To make a perspective drawing, you will make use of a simple principle; lines tend to come together and disappear at vanishing points on the horizon.

Perspectives can be made:

1. To appear below eye level, as though the object were on the floor and you were looking down at it. The object may be on center or to the right or left. Fig. 18-4 (P. 102).

2. To appear at eye level as though the object were on a table at eye height. The base may be on the horizon or the object may be centered on the horizon. Figs. 18-5 and 18-6.

3. To appear above eye level as if the object were on a shelf. Fig. 18-7.

MAKING A PARALLEL PERSPECTIVE

1. Draw a light line across the paper to represent the horizon line. If the object is to be drawn below eye level, place the horizon line about two-thirds of the way up on the page. Mark a point on the line that will represent the vanishing point.

2. Draw the front view of the object as a true view either full size or to scale. This would look exactly like the front view of a working drawing.

3. Draw light construction lines from the four corners of the front view to the vanishing point.

4. Determine the depth of the sides. This can be done by construction procedure but is quite difficult. Therefore, use the trial and error method to locate these points along the construction lines. Try several points until you find one that makes the object look about right. Darken in the lines to form the drawing.

5. Hidden lines are not usually shown in perspective drawings.

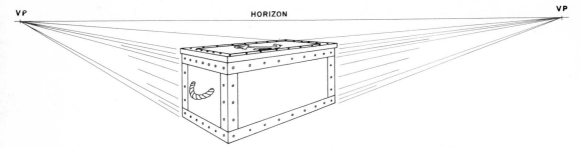

18-4. *An angular perspective as it would appear below eye level.*

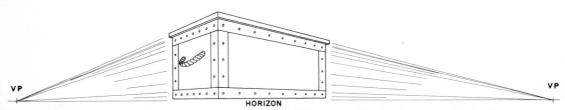

18-5. *An angular perspective as it would appear with the base on the horizon.*

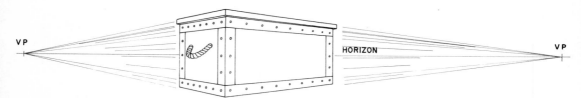

18-6. *An angular perspective with the object centered on the horizon.*

18-7. *An angular perspective with the object above the horizon.*

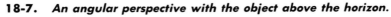
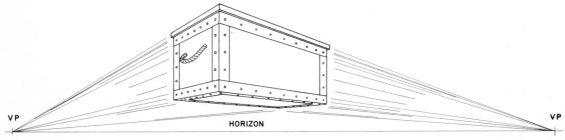

MAKING AN ANGULAR PERSPECTIVE

1. Draw a light construction line across the paper to represent the horizon line. For objects above eye level place the line about one-third of the way up on the page.

2. Mark two points on the horizon to represent the vanishing points.

3. Draw a vertical line to represent one corner (thickness or height) of the object. Fig. 18-8, line AB.

4. Draw construction lines from the ends of this line to both vanishing points.

5. Lay off the length of the object to the right (or left) of the first vertical line. Fig. 18-9. Draw another vertical

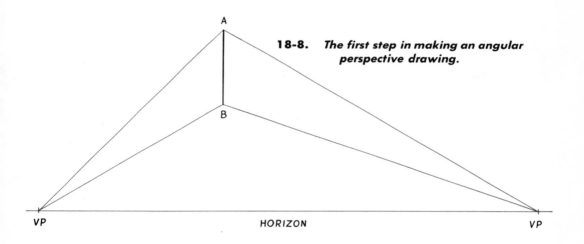

18-8. *The first step in making an angular perspective drawing.*

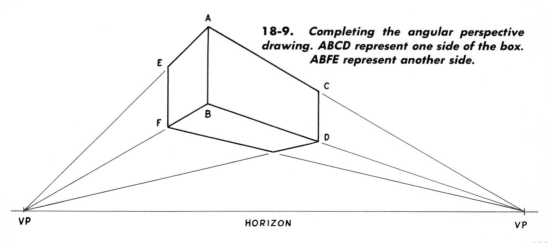

18-9. *Completing the angular perspective drawing. ABCD represent one side of the box. ABFE represent another side.*

line at this point (CD). Lay off the width to the left (or right), and draw another vertical line (EF).

6. Draw construction lines from the bottom end (D and F) of these two lines to the vanishing points on the opposite side. In this case, draw a line from D to the vanishing point on the left side of the page; and draw a line from F to the vanishing point on the right side of the page. Darken in the lines to complete the view.

Unit 19. Making an Isometric Drawing

An isometric drawing is a picture drawing. One corner of the object appears closest to you. The lines that form the sides are 120 degrees apart. Fig. 19-1. Isometric means "equal measure." Do you see why?

An isometric drawing is used primarily for objects that are rectangular in shape. In a single view it provides both a picture of the object and a place to dimension it. Fig. 19-2. Let's make a simple drawing of a rectangular-shaped object such as a basketball bankboard. Fig. 19-3.

1. Draw a light horizontal line. Fig. 19-4. Draw a vertical line to represent one edge of the object (width AB). Fig. 19-3.

2. (a) Draw lines to right and left at an angle of 30 degrees to the horizontal. (b) Mark off AC to represent the length of the bankboard and AD to represent thickness.

3. Draw vertical lines CE and DF.

4. Now, with your 30-60 degree triangle, complete the outline by drawing lines BF, BE, FG, and EG. Notice that all of these lines are drawn their true length since they are isometric lines.

5. Hidden or invisible lines are not usually shown on isometric drawings.

19-1. *The three lines used as a base for constructing an isometric. Notice that they are 120 degrees apart. Two lines are drawn at an angle of 30 degrees to the horizontal.*

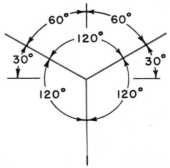

NON-ISOMETRIC LINES

Many objects are not true rectangles. For example, the plastic pen holder shown in Fig. 19-5 has one corner cut off for the pen hole. To make a drawing of this kind it is necessary to enclose the object in an "isometric box." Fig. 19-6 (P. 106). Measure from the corners A and B and mark the location of the slanted lines (F and C). Connect points FC, CD, FE and ED. Lines CD and FE will not be true length. They are called *non-isometric lines*. Non-isometric lines must be drawn by locating the

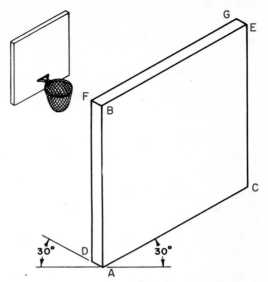

19-3. *An isometric drawing of a basketball bankboard.*

19-2. *An isometric drawing of a knife rack. The over-all dimensions are* $1/2'' \times 6^1/2'' \times 11^3/4''$. *The top and bottom are* $3/8''$ *thick. The back is* $1/4''$ *in thickness.*

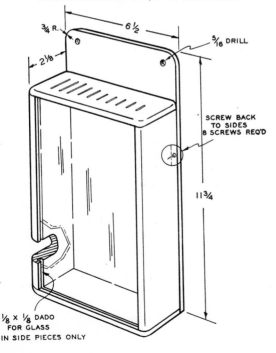

¾ R.

6 ½

$5/16$ DRILL

2⅛

SCREW BACK
TO SIDES
8 SCREWS REQ'D

11¾

⅛ X ⅛ DADO
FOR GLASS
IN SIDE PIECES ONLY

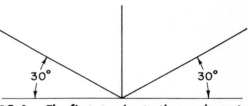

19-4. *The first step in starting an isometric drawing.*

19-5. *This plastic pen holder has several non-isometric lines. Which are they?*

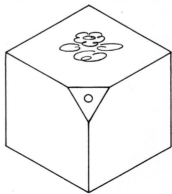

ends of the lines on isometric lines and connecting the points with a straightedge.

DRAWING CIRCLES IN ISOMETRIC

A circle in isometric is really an ellipse. For this reason the isometric drawing is not the best one for objects that are circular in shape. However, to draw a circle in isometric, proceed as follows. Fig. 19-7.

1. Draw a square in isometric, ABCD.

2. Divide the sides in half and mark these points E, F, G, and H.

3. Draw light construction lines AE, AF, CG, and CH. Mark the points of intersection I and J.

4. Adjust a compass to a radius equal to JF. Place the point of the compass at J and draw the arc FH.

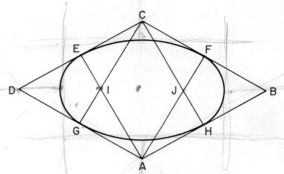

19-7. *Drawing a circle in isometric.*

Place the point of the compass at I and draw the arc EG.

5. Adjust the compass to a radius of AE. Place the point of the compass at C and draw the arc HG. Place the point of the compass at A and draw the arc EF. This will complete the isometric circle.

6. To draw isometric circles in a vertical plane for right or left surfaces of an object, follow the suggestions given in Fig. 19-8.

EXPLODED ISOMETRIC

A type of isometric drawing that is particularly useful for construction or for assembling parts is an exploded isometric. It is valuable because it shows each part in great detail. It also shows how the whole thing goes together. Look at the exploded isometric drawing of stacking cabinets shown in Fig. 19-9 and see how each dimension is clearly shown. You can also see how each part must be put together to make the assembly.

19-6. *To draw non-isometric lines, the object must be enclosed in an isometric box.*

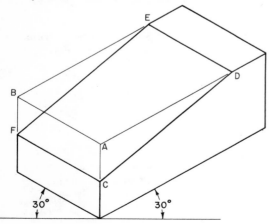

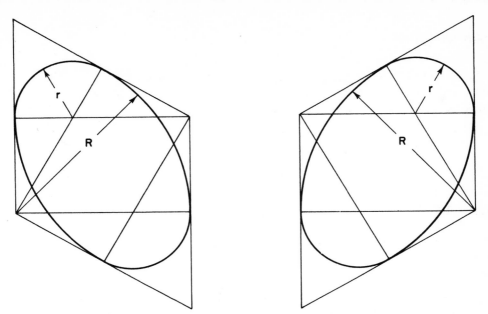

19-8. *Drawing isometric circles to the left and right.*

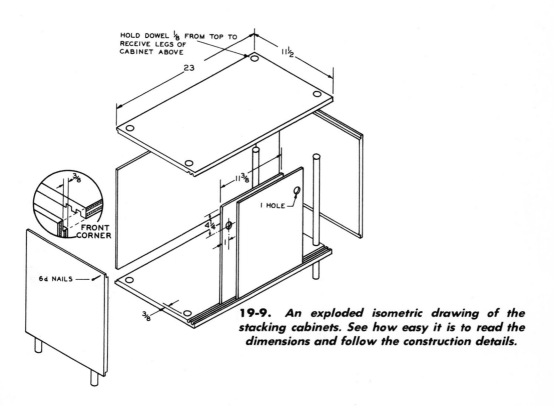

HOLD DOWEL ⅛ FROM TOP TO
RECEIVE LEGS OF
CABINET ABOVE

23

11½

11⅜

1 HOLE

4¼

3/8

FRONT
CORNER

6d NAILS

3/8

19-9. *An exploded isometric drawing of the
stacking cabinets. See how easy it is to read the
dimensions and follow the construction details.*

IRREGULAR CURVES IN ISOMETRIC

If part of the object to be drawn in isometric contains irregular curves, proceed as follows:

Make a one-view drawing of the irregular surface on squared paper. Mark the vertical and horizontal lines with letters and numbers as you would for enlarging a pattern. Fig. 19-10, top drawing. Now draw an isometric box, with one face of the box covered with squares. Transfer the points from the view drawing to the isometric box until enough points are secured. Then use a French curve to draw the curves. Fig. 19-10, bottom drawing.

ANGLES IN ISOMETRIC

To lay out an angle in isometric, do the following:

Make a one-view drawing showing the angle. Draw an isometric box. Transfer the actual measurements (X and Y) from the view drawing. Draw the angle. Fig. 19-11.

DIMENSIONING IN ISOMETRIC

The same general rules for dimensioning working drawings are followed in isometric. The dimension lines should always be parallel to the object lines. The extension and dimension lines should be outside the object whenever possible.

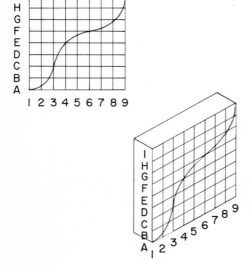

19-10. *Drawing a curve in isometric. The curve is first drawn as a one-view drawing and then the points transferred to the isometric box. A French curve is needed.*

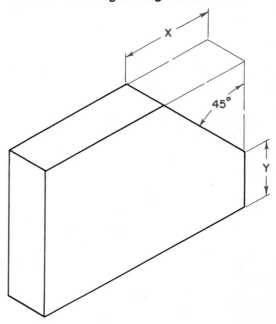

19-11. *Drawing an angle in isometric.*

Unit 20. Making an Oblique or Cabinet Drawing

Another type of picture drawing is called an oblique drawing. Oblique means "slanting" or "inclined." That's exactly what the drawing is. One side of the object appears closest to you. The top and right or left side slant away from you.

KINDS OF OBLIQUE

The two kinds of oblique drawings are *cavalier* and *cabinet*. In a *cavalier* drawing the true lengths of the side and top are measured off along the inclined lines. Notice, in Fig. 20-1, that this looks to the eye as if the top and side are longer than they really are. For this reason the cavalier drawing is seldom used. In the *cabinet* drawing this is corrected. Fig. 20-1. If an object is a true rectangle, the front side is drawn exactly as a working drawing. This surface is shown by vertical and horizontal lines of true length. The other surfaces are formed by drawing inclined lines at an angle of 30 to 45 degrees, but usually 45 degrees, to the right or left. Half the true length is measured off on the inclined lines to complete the drawing. The correct dimension, however, is always given.

Cabinet drawing was so named because it is the favorite of the cabinet-

20-1. *A cube drawn as a cavalier oblique and as a cabinet oblique. Which looks more like a cube? This is a good illustration of optical illusion.*

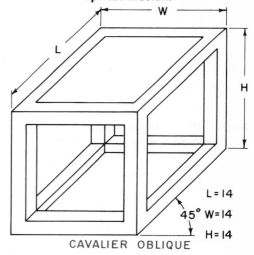

W
L
H
L = 14
45° W = 14
H = 14

CAVALIER OBLIQUE

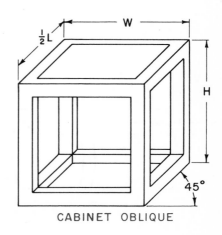

½ L
W
H
45°

CABINET OBLIQUE

maker. It's an excellent kind of picture drawing for rectangular cabinets, chests, and tables.

POINTS TO REMEMBER

1. If a cabinet drawing contains circular parts, always draw the circle on the surface that appears nearest you. It will then be a true circle in size and shape. For example, to draw the head of a croquet mallet, make the circle a part of the side nearest you as shown in Fig. 20-2. Circles on the top or right or left surface would be ellipses, as in isometric drawings.

2. If a long object, such as a win-dow box, is drawn in cabinet, always place the long side as part of the surface nearest you, never the short side. Fig: 20-3. Notice that rules 1 and 2 sometimes clash. If they do, the first rule is the more important. The croquet mallet is an example.

3. To make a cabinet drawing that is above eye level, such as this high kitchen cabinet, Fig. 20-4, draw the inclined lines down at an angle of 45 degrees, instead of up.

To make a cabinet drawing, proceed as follows:

20-3. *The right and wrong way to draw a long flower box. Notice that the long side is a part of the surface nearest you.*

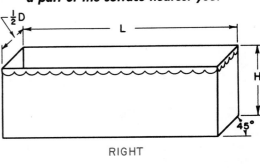

RIGHT

20-2. *The right and wrong way to draw the head of a croquet mallet.*

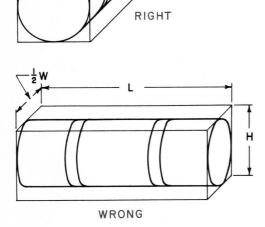

RIGHT

WRONG

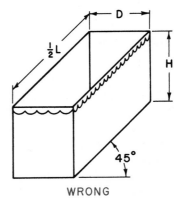

WRONG

1. Select the side that makes the best front surface.

2. Draw this front surface as you would draw the front view of a working drawing.

3. Draw inclined · lines from the front view at an angle of 45 degrees to

the right or left to form the top and side.

4. Lay off *only half the true length* on these inclined lines.

5. Draw the horizontal and vertical lines from these points to complete the outline of the object.

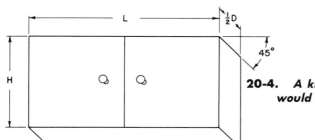

20-4. *A kitchen cabinet above eye level would be drawn as shown here.*

Unit 21. Detail and Assembly Drawings

Working drawings are of two kinds—*detail* and *assembly*. Assembly drawings show how the parts go together. These vary a great deal in the amount of information included. A detail drawing always gives all of the information necessary to construct a particular part.

KINDS OF ASSEMBLY DRAWINGS

There are several kinds of assembly drawings. Each has a particular purpose. Some of the most common are:

1. Working assembly drawings. This type gives complete information

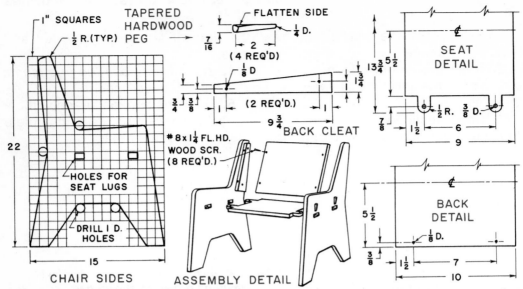

21-1. *A working assembly drawing for a child's chair. Notice that there is complete information given on how to build and assemble it.*

on how to make each part and how it fits with the next part. For example, most woodworking drawings are working assembly drawings. These are usually *view* drawings although *pictorial* drawings might also be used. Fig. 21-1. One drawing includes all the information.

2. Outline assembly drawings. This is an outline drawing showing how the parts go together. It may be either a pictorial or view drawing. Its main purpose is to show how to put the object together. This type is often used with detail drawings. For example, to make the C-clamp, Fig. 21-2, a pictorial assembly drawing and detail drawings of each part are provided. The parts are usually numbered or lettered and the same numbers or letters placed near each of the detail drawings.

3. Sub-assembly drawings. This shows how a part of a larger object is assembled. For example, Fig. 21-3 shows how each part must be assembled to form the fork and handlebar assembly of a minibike.

4. Installation diagram. This is usually a simple drawing of the object with only a few measurements necessary to install it. In Figs. 21-4 and 21-5 (P. 114), you see a model aircraft engine-propeller and an installation diagram. Enough information is given to make it possible to install the engine in a model plane.

DETAIL DRAWINGS

A detail drawing shows everything about a single part that is necessary to build or make it. It must include the exact shape, the exact dimensions, and any other information needed

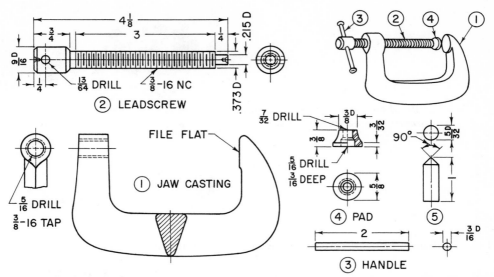

21-2. *A detail drawing of each part of the C-clamp. Notice that the assembly drawing is numbered and the numbers are shown beside each of the detail drawings.*

21-3. *Parts of a minibike: fork and handlebar assembly.*

1	Fork Support Complete
3	Fork Spring
4	Lower Fork Pipe R.H.
5	Fork Upper Bushing
6	Fork Lower Bushing
8	Fork Boot
9	Front Fender Complete
10	Screw 6 × 12
11	6 mm Spring Washer
12	6 mm Washer
13	Inner Race Upper
14	Race Lock Nut
15	Fork Handle Holder
16	Handle Holder Washer
17	Bolt 10 × 30 mm
20	Handle Complete L.H.
21	Handle Complete R.H.
22	Handle Knob Complete
23	Lower Fork Pipe L.H.
24	Inner Race Lower

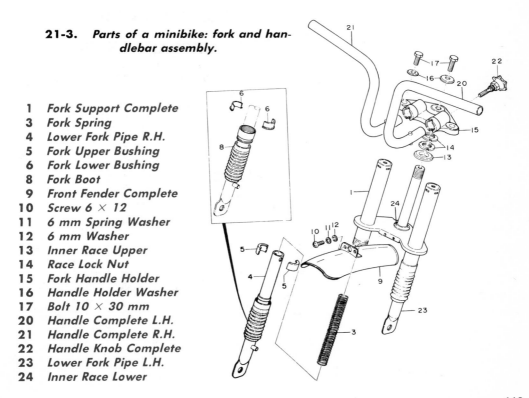

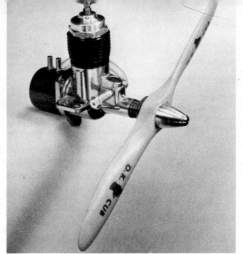

21-4. *This photograph shows the model aircraft engine in Fig. 21-5.*

21-5. *This installation diagram is needed to build a model airplane in which this engine might be installed.*

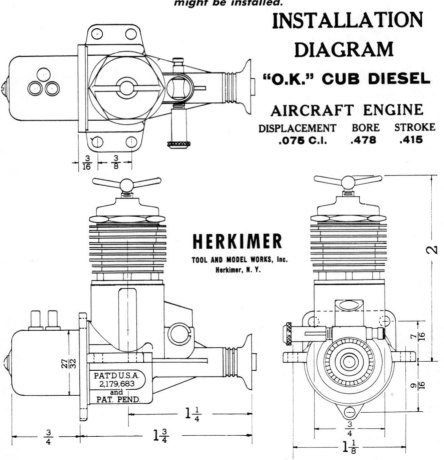

INSTALLATION
DIAGRAM
"O.K." CUB DIESEL
AIRCRAFT ENGINE

DISPLACEMENT	BORE	STROKE
.075 C.I.	.478	.415

HERKIMER

TOOL AND MODEL WORKS, Inc.
Herkimer, N. Y.

PAT D U.S.A.
2,179,683
and
PAT. PEND.

about the kind of material to use, the finish, and other details.

There are several suggestions for making an accurate detail drawing:

1. If the object contains several detail drawings, make each of them to the same scale. If the part is very small, make the detail drawing double size.

2. Place the detail drawing on the page so it is convenient to read.

3. Place the dimensions on each so they can be read easily.

4. Select the views that will show the detail best. Use only enough views to show it well. Sometimes one is enough and at other times two or three are needed to show everything.

5. "Block in" the drawing with light construction lines.

6. Complete the detail drawing, including all necessary information. If the object is small and contains few parts, both the detail drawing for each part and the assembly drawing may be shown on the same page.

A complete set of working drawings for a large object will include several assembly drawings plus a detail drawing for each part of the object.

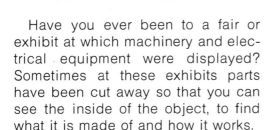

Unit 22. Making a Sectional View

Have you ever been to a fair or exhibit at which machinery and electrical equipment were displayed? Sometimes at these exhibits parts have been cut away so that you can see the inside of the object, to find what it is made of and how it works.

If you want to show in a drawing how the inside of something looks, you can make a sectional view, or "section." This is done by imagining that a part has been cut away, as an apple would be cut with a knife. Figs. 22-1 and 22-2 (P. 116). This kind of view is a great help to those who read the drawing. It makes it simpler and points out important details.

MAKING A FULL SECTION

Sections are used with working drawings. Often the front view is shown in section and the side or top view shows where it has been cut. When the front half is cut away it is called a *full section*. Fig. 22-3. On the other view a *cutting plane line* shows where the object has been cut. This line is made up of one long dash (usually 12 to 20 mm—$\frac{1}{2}$" to $\frac{3}{4}$"—long) and two short dashes (about 2

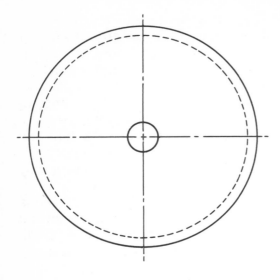

to 3 mm—$1/16''$ to $1/8''$). Fig. 22-3. Arrows are drawn at the ends of this line to show the direction in which you are viewing the cut surface. Letters such as A-A are placed at the ends of these arrows. Under the section view the note "Section A-A" is lettered. Fig. 22-3. This is done so that on more complicated drawings the second can be B-B, the third C-C, etc.

In some cases the cutting plane line is offset instead of straight to show better the details in section. Fig. 22-4.

22-3. *A full-section view of the fishing-line spool. Notice the arrows and the cutting plane line on the top view. It shows the direction in which you are looking at the front view. The note "Section A-A" is placed under the section.*

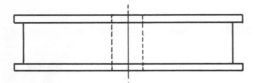

22-1. *A standard two-view drawing of a fishing-line spool.*

22-2. *Cutting the spool. Of course, in drawing, this is done only in imagination. This would make a full-section view.*

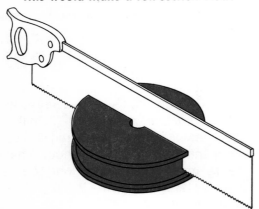

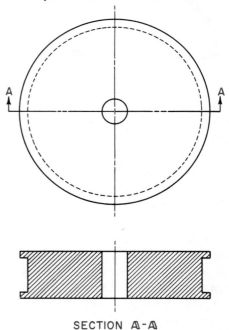

SECTION A-A

On the section view all areas that are *cut* are covered with *section lines* or *crosshatching*. These are thin parallel lines at 45 degrees, spaced about $1/32''$ to $1/8''$ apart. Hidden lines are not drawn on the section view unless needed for complete description.

OTHER SECTIONAL VIEWS

When only half the front section is cut away it is called a *half section*. Fig. 22-5. This is used when you wish to show what the outside and inside look like on the same view. Usually invisible lines are not shown on the outside portion of the view. When a part is torn or broken away it is called a *broken out section*. This is particularly useful when showing certain details on a drawing. For example, see how well this shows the shape of the holes on a rivet set. Fig. 22-6.

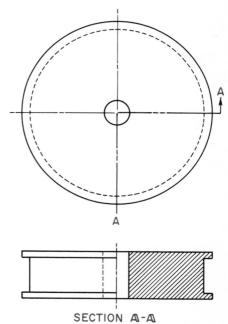

SECTION A-A

22-5. *A half section. Hidden lines are shown on the unsectioned side only if required for clearness. Here the hidden line was added so that you can easily see the hole.*

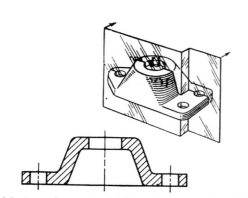

22-4. *The cutting plane line may be off-set to show certain details better, as is done here with a machine part.*

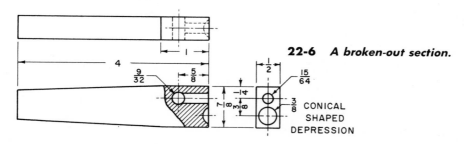

22-6 *A broken-out section.*

CONICAL SHAPED DEPRESSION

Oftentimes a section will be *revolved* to show the cross-section shape of the object, such as the crowbar shown in Fig. 23-5. Another section that may be used is the *removed* or *detail section*. This is similar to a revolved section. A cutting plane line is drawn in a certain location and the shape of that area shown in a detail or removed section to one side of the object.

SYMBOLS FOR MATERIALS

Instead of using the crosshatching or section lining, symbols have been developed to identify various kinds of materials. In Fig. 23-5 the symbol on the revolved section indicates that the material is steel. While these symbols do show the kind of material, the information is not specific enough. A note must be added to give more definite specifications for the material. Fig. 22-7.

POINTS TO REMEMBER

1. Use section lining or crosshatching for most drawings.

2. If the section view shows two or more parts, draw section lines at different angles and in different directions to identify the parts. On two parts the lines should be at right angles. Fig. 22-8. Always draw the lines in the same direction on the part as it appears in the drawing.

3. Never section bolts, nuts, rivets, and other fasteners. Fig. 22-8.

4. Sections that are too thin for crosshatching (sheet metal and others) can be shown solid.

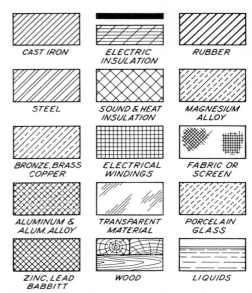

22-7. Symbols that can be used instead of crosshatching or section lining on assembly drawings.

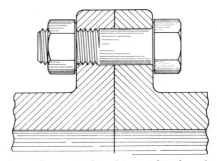

22-8. The crosshatching clearly shows that there are two different parts here. Notice that the machine bolt and nut are not sectioned.

5. On simple symmetrical objects, the cutting plane line, letters, and arrows need not be used. The center line can serve as the cutting plane line.

6. When sectioning objects that are irregular, such as the spokes of this handwheel, Fig. 22-9, imagine that one spoke is rotated until it is parallel to the plane of the section. Do not section the spokes.

7. Do not section thin ribs and other parts that might make the section view confusing.

8. Section lining does not have to cover large areas completely. Place the section lining around the outline.

CONVENTIONAL BREAKS

It is often difficult to draw long objects to their full size. To save space, conventional breaks are used to shorten the view. See how the break lines are made for round and rectangular-shaped parts. Fig. 22-10.

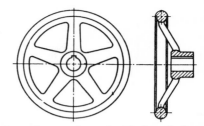

22-9. *The spokes of this handwheel are not sectioned.*

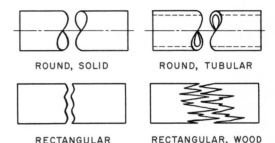

ROUND, SOLID   ROUND, TUBULAR

RECTANGULAR   RECTANGULAR, WOOD

22-10. *Conventional breaks.*

Unit 23. Drawing an Auxiliary View

In making a working drawing of an object that has a slanted or inclined surface, you have a special problem. For example, the meter case, Fig. 23-1 (P. 120), has no main view (front, top, or side) that shows the face to the correct size and shape. The round part appears as an ellipse on both the top and right side, or end, views. It is easy to see why this is so. In a three-view drawing all lines of the object must be at right angles to each other to appear true shape. A slanting surface (made of oblique lines) will always be shorter on any of the main views. To correct this an auxiliary (extra) view is made. This is a view you would see if you looked directly at the slanting face. Fig. 23-2. Auxiliary views, then, are used primarily in

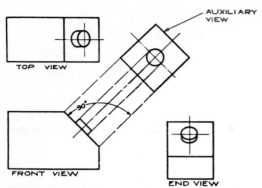

23-1. *An auxiliary view of a meter case. Notice that only in the auxiliary view is the round part shown in its true shape.*

making a working drawing of irregularly shaped objects.

How many common objects can you think of that would require an auxiliary view if they were drawn? A standard dial telephone or an antenna regulator that has a slanted face are two of them.

Auxiliary views are needed mostly in machine drawing. Many parts in mechanical and electrical objects,

23-2. *The auxiliary view, or projection, as it is sometimes called, is drawn as shown here.*

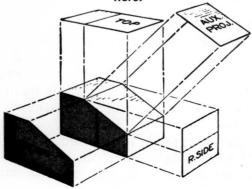

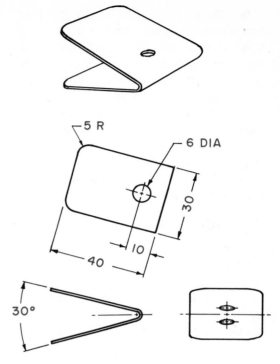

ALL DIMENSIONS IN mm.

23-3. *A drawing with an auxiliary view for a simple object—a sheet-metal whistle.*

such as brackets, connectors, or pipes, are bent at an obtuse or acute angle. Auxiliary views are needed to show these parts in true size and shape. Fig. 23-3.

KINDS OF AUXILIARY VIEWS

The shape of the object determines how the auxiliary view must be drawn. Irregularly shaped objects are of three general types:

1. Those in which the slanted surface is from the *top* to the *right* (or left) side.

2. Those in which the slanted surface is from the *top* to the *front.*

3. Those in which the slanted surface is from the *front* to the *right* (or left) side.

An auxiliary view is always drawn or projected from the view in which the slanted surface is shown as a line. For example, if the slanted surface is from the top to the right side, the auxiliary view is drawn or projected from the front view.

MAKING AN AUXILIARY VIEW

An auxiliary view is good for a project such as this pen holder. Fig. 23-4. Notice that the slanted surface is from the top to the right side. Therefore the auxiliary view will be drawn from the front view.

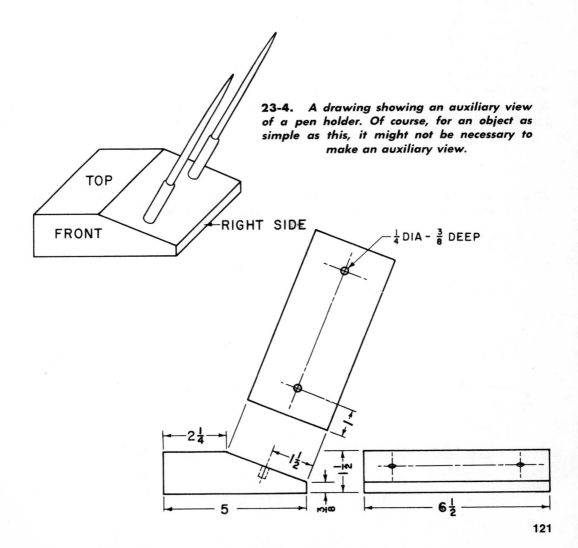

23-4. *A drawing showing an auxiliary view of a pen holder. Of course, for an object as simple as this, it might not be necessary to make an auxiliary view.*

1. Draw the front view of the pen holder.

2. Draw the right side or top view. Usually only one additional view is needed. In this case it is better to draw the right-side view.

3. Draw light construction lines at right angles to the slant line on the front view. You now have the width of the auxiliary view.

4. Determine the length of the auxiliary view from the side view. Measure this length along one construction line and draw two light lines that are parallel to the slant lines on the front view. Locate the position of the holes using the front and side views for reference.

5. Complete the auxiliary view.

POINTS TO REMEMBER

1. In an auxiliary view draw only the slanted surface and not the entire view.

2. *Only one or two views are necessary in addition to the auxiliary view.* Fig. 23-4. Only in rare cases are all three views and an auxiliary view drawn.

3. The main views (front, top, and right side) may have to be placed farther apart than is normal so that they will not interfere with the auxiliary view. In addition, enough space must be provided for dimensioning the drawing.

4. An auxiliary view is needed for each slanted or inclined surface of the object. Fig. 23-5.

23-5. *An auxiliary view is needed for both ends of this crowbar. Notice that the revolved section of the crowbar makes use of symbols to show that the material is steel.*

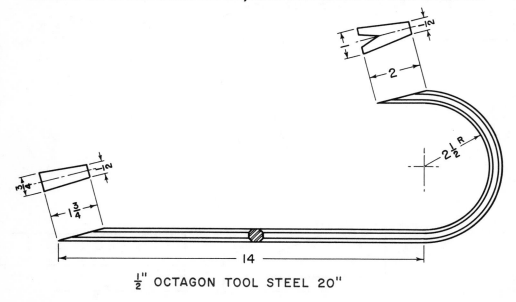

$\frac{1}{2}''$ OCTAGON TOOL STEEL 20''

5. If the object is symmetrical, draw a center line parallel to the slanted line and a convenient distance away. Use this line as a reference for making the auxiliary view.

6. If the auxiliary view contains an irregular line or curve, obtain the measurements from one of the main views and transfer them to the auxiliary view.

Unit 24. Doing Useful Geometric Construction

Many drawings and layouts contain geometric shapes. Some of these, such as a circle, square, triangle, or rectangle, are very simple. Many times you need to draw certain simple geometric constructions. There are many other constructions used by engineers and drafters, but a few of the simpler ones include:

1. Bisecting a line or an arc (dividing it into two equal parts).

a. To bisect the line or arc AB, adjust a compass to a radius greater than one-half AB. Fig. 24-1.

b. With A and B as centers draw arcs that intersect at C and D.

c. Draw line CD. This will divide the line or arc AB into two equal parts.

2. Dividing a line into several equal parts. One procedure is used frequently on the job site to divide material of odd width into several equal parts. Suppose you want to divide a board 5″ wide into three equal parts. Hold the rule at an angle across the board with one end of the rule on one edge and the 6″ mark on the other. You can also divide using a metric rule. Fig. 24-2 (P. 124). Mark a point at 2″ and at 4″. Another procedure is used in drawing. Fig. 24-3.

a. Draw a line, AB, or any length.

b. Draw a line, AC, at an angle to AB.

24-1. *Bisecting a line or an arc.*

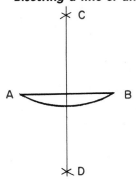

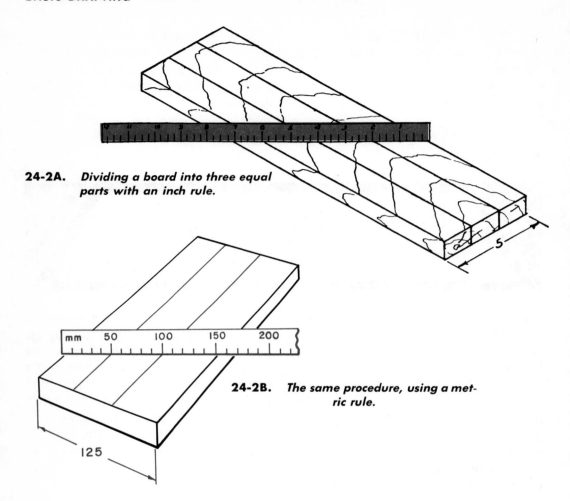

24-2A. *Dividing a board into three equal parts with an inch rule.*

24-2B. *The same procedure, using a metric rule.*

c. Starting at point A, lay off several equal divisions with a dividers, compass, or rule. The number of divisions is equal to the number of parts into which you wish to divide line AB.

d. Draw a line from the end of C to point B.

e. Draw lines parallel to BC at the divisions on AC. These lines will intersect AB and divide it into equal parts.

24-3. *Dividing a line into several equal parts.*

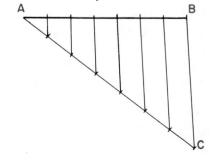

3. Bisecting an angle.

a. Draw the given angle BAC. Fig. 24-4.

b. Adjust the compass to a radius of about ³/₄″.

c. With A as the center, strike an arc intersecting AB at D and AC at E.

d. Adjust the compass to a radius of more than half ED.

e. With D and E as centers, strike two arcs that intersect at F.

f. Draw the line AF to divide the angle into equal parts.

4. Drawing an arc at a square corner. In many projects, you will make rounded corners to improve the appearance of the object and for utili-

ty. In geometry this would be called drawing an arc tangent to lines at 90 degrees. Fig. 24-5.

a. Draw the two lines, AB and AC, that intersect at A.

b. Determine the radius of the arc.

c. Measure in from lines AC and AB this distance and draw parallel lines to these lines that intersect at D.

d. Use D as the center and draw the arc.

e. This procedure may be followed in the shop as shown in Fig. 24-6.

5. Drawing an arc tangent to two lines that are not at right an-

24-6. *The shop method for drawing an arc at a square corner. Determine the radius of the arc. Mark this distance from the corner on the adjacent side and end. Hold a try square against the edge and end and draw two lines to locate the center. Use dividers to draw the arc.*

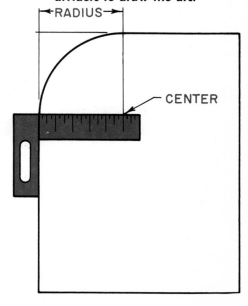

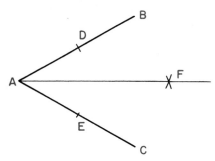

24-4. *Bisecting an angle.*

24-5. *Drawing an arc at a square corner.*

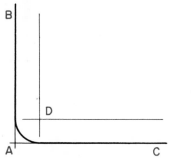

gles. Fig. 24-7. Sometimes an irregularly shaped object has a rounded corner. This can be drawn as follows:

a. Draw two lines to represent the edges of the materials, AB and AC.

b. Determine the desired radius of the arc.

c. Adjust the compass or dividers to this amount.

d. At several points along both lines, draw small arcs e, f, g, h, etc.

e. Draw straight lines tangent to these arcs until they intersect at O.

f. Using O as center, strike the arc.

6. Drawing tangent arcs. Many irregular-shaped objects such as machine parts or Early American furniture pieces have arcs or circles that are tangent. Figs. 24-8 and 24-9. Arcs or circles are tangent when they touch at only one point but do not intersect. To join a series of arcs, proceed as follows (Fig. 24-10):

a. With O as center and R1 as radius, draw the first arc.

b. With P as center and R2 as radius draw the second arc.

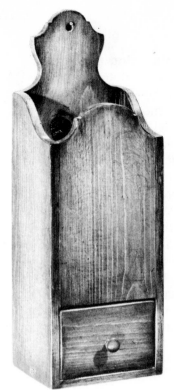

24-8. *This spice holder has a back panel detail that has tangent arcs.*

24-9A. *A drawing of the back panel detail showing tangent arcs.*

24-7. *Drawing an arc to two lines that are not at right angles.*

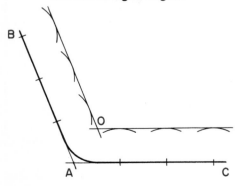

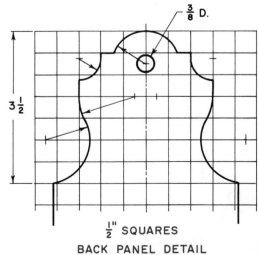

$\frac{3}{8}$ D.

$3\frac{1}{2}$

$\frac{1}{2}$" SQUARES

BACK PANEL DETAIL

c. With O as center and R1 plus R3 as radius, strike a small arc at the approximate center location for the third arc.

d. With P as center and R2 plus R3 as radius, strike a second arc that intersects at X with the first small arc.

e. With X as center and R3 as radius, strike the last arc.

7. Drawing an arc with a given radius tangent to a straight line and a circle or arc. Fig. 24-11. The procedure is used often in drawing machine parts. Proceed as follows:

a. Draw line AB to the desired length.

b. With B as center and with a compass adjusted to radius R1, draw arc CD.

c. Draw a line (EF) the given radius (R2) above and parallel to line AB.

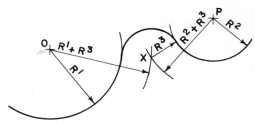

24-10. *Drawing a series of tangent arcs.*

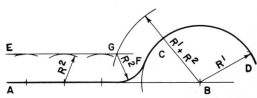

24-11. *Drawing an arc with a given radius tangent to a straight line and a circle or arc.*

d. With B as center and with R1 plus R2 as radius, strike an arc that intersects the parallel line at G.

e. With G as center and with the compass set at R2, draw the arc that joins the straight line with the arc or circle.

8. Drawing an octagon. An octagon has eight equal sides and angles. Fig. 24-12 (P. 128). It is often used as a shape for metal or wood projects such as wastepaper baskets, hot-dish holders and trays. It might also be the shape of a ticket in printing.

a. Draw a square of the size of the octagon.

b. Draw diagonal lines AB and CD.

c. Adjust the compass to half the length of one of the diagonal lines.

24-9B. *A metric drawing of the same back panel.*

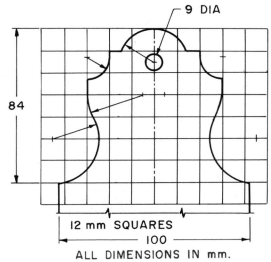

9 DIA

84

12 mm SQUARES

100

ALL DIMENSIONS IN mm.

BACK PANEL DETAIL

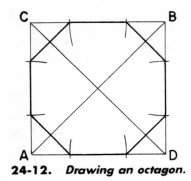

24-12. *Drawing an octagon.*

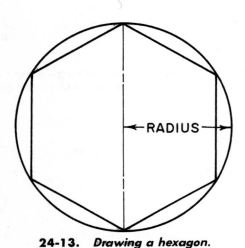

←RADIUS→

24-13. *Drawing a hexagon.*

chisel from hexagon-shaped stock. The heads of many bolts and nuts are hexagons. To draw a hexagon:

a. Draw a circle with a radius equal to one side of the hexagon.

b. Set the compass equal to the radius of the circle.

c. Start at any point on the circle and draw an arc.

d. Move the point of the compass to this point and strike another arc. Then divide the circle into six equal parts.

e. Connect these points with straight lines.

10. Drawing an ellipse. An ellipse is a regular curve that has two different diameters. It is a flattened circle. You find this shape often in the tops of tables, on plaques, and in the backs of lamps. Wherever anything round is shown in isometric, draw an ellipse. Fig. 24-14.

a. Draw the major and minor axes, AB and CD, bisecting each other at right angles.

d. Using points A, B, C, and D as centers, strike arcs intersecting the sides.

e. Connect the points where the arcs intersect the square.

9. Drawing a hexagon. A hexagon has six equal sides and angles. Fig. 24-13. It's another shape we use often in shop work. For example, you might make a center punch or cold

24-14. *Drawing an ellipse. This method can be used only if CD is at least two-thirds of AB.*

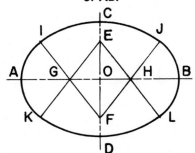

b. Lay out OE and OF, which are equal to AB minus CD.

c. Make OH and OG equal to three-fourths of OE or OF.

d. Draw lines EK, EL, FI, FJ.

e. Using E and F as centers and ED as radius, strike arcs IJ and KL.

f. Use G and H as centers and GA as radius. Strike arcs IK and JL.

There is another shop method of drawing the ellipse that is very simple. You will want to use it.

1. Draw the major and minor axes AB and CD. Fig. 24-15.

2. Set the dividers equal to half the longest diameter.

3. Using D as center strike an arc intersecting AB at X and Y.

4. Place a pin at X, Y and D. Tie a string around these three pins.

5. Take the pin at D away and put a pencil point in its place.

6. Hold the point of the pencil tight against the string. Carefully move the pencil around the board, drawing the ellipse.

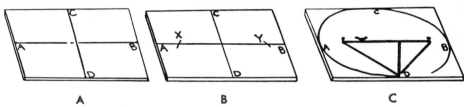

24-15. *A shop method for drawing an ellipse.*

Unit 25. Architectural Drawings

A drawing of a building in which people live or work is called an *architectural* drawing. This is a very special kind of drawing done by architects—people who plan buildings. Becoming an architect requires at least four or five years of college training and several years of practical experience in an architect's office. You should not expect to design and draw complete architectural plans yourself, but you can learn something about planning and designing a home. It is very helpful to know how to make preliminary or first rough plans for such things as a new cabin or house or an addition to a home. Most important, you can learn how to read house plans.

Building construction is one of the largest industries in our country. There are more people employed in skilled trades in building construction than in any other area of activity. There are more than fifteen specialized, skilled building trades. If you become interested in any profession or trade in the building industry, you will need to learn a good deal more about making and reading architectural drawings.

MAKING A ROOM ARRANGEMENT OR LAB LAYOUT

A very simple kind of architectural drawing is a room arrangement or plan. Suppose you have built or bought a new piece of furniture for your room. You will want to arrange it without actually moving all the furniture around. You can do the following:

1. Select a piece of squared or cross-sectioned paper that has four or eight squares to the inch. Follow a scale of $1/4''$ to the foot or a metric scale to make your drawings.

2. Measure your room to find its size. Draw the outline of the room on the paper. Show all the doors and windows to the proper scale.

3. Make cutouts or templates to scale of all the pieces of furniture. Fig. 25-1 shows the cutouts for many pieces of furniture. Draw these on

cardboard. Letter in the name of each one and cut them out.

4. Place the cutouts on the room outline. Remember what the room is to be used for. Move the cutouts around several times until you find the best location for the furniture. Remember that the plan is a view of the room as you look at it from above. Fig. 25-2 (P. 132).

5. When you have a good arrangement, attach the cutouts to the outline with rubber cement.

6. This kind of planning is done in schools and industries in making layouts of industrial education laboratories and factories. You can do it to plan a home workshop in an area in your basement or garage.

PLANNING AN ADDITION

Often a house is not big enough for a growing family. Suppose a family wants to plan an activity room in the basement, add a garage, enclose a porch, or finish a bedroom in the attic. Fig. 25-3. This is a good chance to become acquainted with architectural drawing.

If the room is to be finished inside the house, you will find its size by measuring the space. If it is to be outside the house like a porch, extra room or garage, you will need to decide on the size of the addition and its location. Size and location will depend on what the room is to be used for. It is best to make a floor plan and then discuss it with the others in the family. This rough plan should be drawn to scale on squared paper.

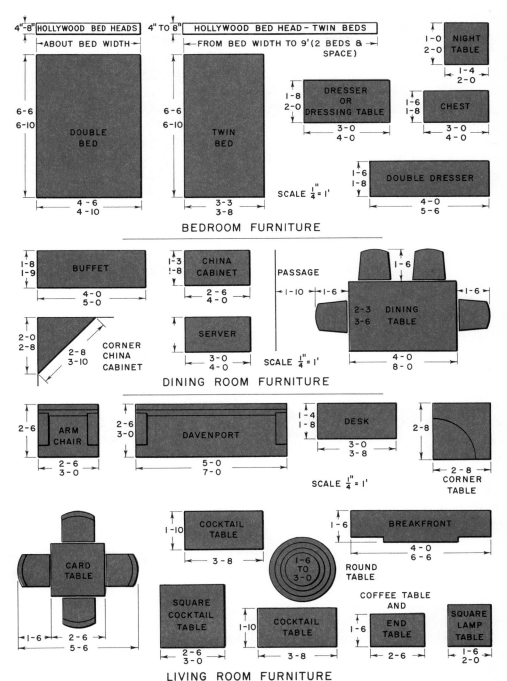

BEDROOM FURNITURE

4"-8" HOLLYWOOD BED HEADS

←ABOUT BED WIDTH→

DOUBLE BED
6-6
6-10
4-6
4-10

4" TO 8" HOLLYWOOD BED HEAD – TWIN BEDS

←FROM BED WIDTH TO 9' (2 BEDS & SPACE)→

TWIN BED
6-6
6-10
3-3
3-8

NIGHT TABLE
1-0
2-0
1-4
2-0

DRESSER OR DRESSING TABLE
1-8
2-0
3-0
4-0

CHEST
1-6
1-8
3-0
4-0

DOUBLE DRESSER
1-6
1-8
4-0
5-6

SCALE ¼" = 1'

DINING ROOM FURNITURE

BUFFET
1-8
1-9
4-0
5-0

CHINA CABINET
1-3
1-8
2-6
4-0

CORNER CHINA CABINET
2-0
2-8
2-8
3-10

SERVER
3-0
4-0

PASSAGE
1-10
1-6

DINING TABLE
1-6
2-3
3-6
4-0
8-0

SCALE ¼" = 1'

LIVING ROOM FURNITURE

ARM CHAIR
2-6
2-6
3-0

DAVENPORT
2-6
3-0
5-0
7-0

DESK
1-4
1-8
3-0
3-8

CORNER TABLE
2-8
2-8

SCALE ¼" = 1'

CARD TABLE
1-6
2-6
5-6

COCKTAIL TABLE
1-10
3-8

SQUARE COCKTAIL TABLE
2-6
3-0

COCKTAIL TABLE
1-10
3-8

ROUND TABLE
1-6 TO 3-0

BREAKFRONT
1-6
4-0
6-6

COFFEE TABLE AND

END TABLE
1-6
2-6

SQUARE LAMP TABLE
1-6
2-0

25-1. *Common sizes of furniture to use in making templates. Scale is ¹/₄" = 1'.*

Make the floor plan as follows:

1. Measure the area to be included in the new addition.

2. Decide on the scale. Usually a scale of $1/2''$ to $1'$ or $1/4''$ to $1'$ is used.

3. Draw the outline of the room or addition.

4. Locate all openings such as windows and doors. Draw these to scale.

5. Draw in any obstructions such as chimneys, walls, and pipes.

6. Draw in any partitions such as closets or cabinets.

7. Darken in the outline.

8. Add the dimensions.

After you have decided on the exact size and shape, you can take the rough drawing to a lumberyard. Here an architect or building consultant will make a more detailed plan for you. He or she will also help you to decide on the materials.

KINDS OF CONSTRUCTION

Nine out of ten homes in the United States are of wood-framed construction. While many are covered with shingles, brick, aluminum, plastic, or stucco, they are still considered to be

25-2. *Here is a typical plan view of a house showing the furniture arrangement.*

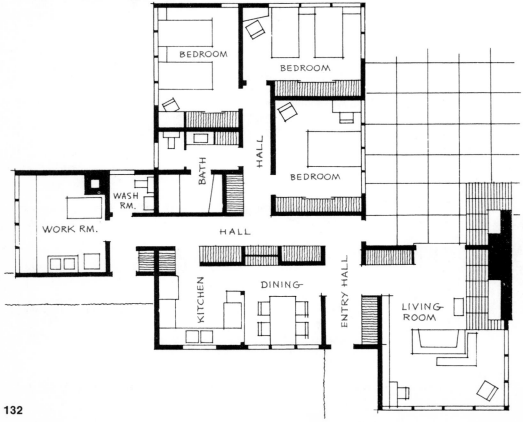

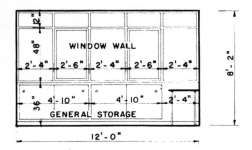

ELEVATION I

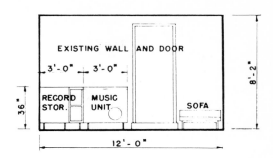

ELEVATION 2

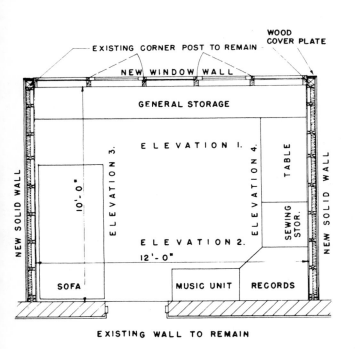

FLOOR PLAN

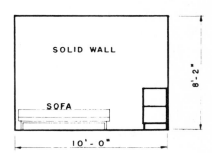

ELEVATION 3

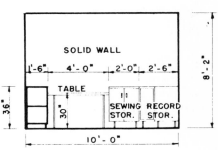

ELEVATION 4

25-3. *Floor plan and elevations for a new room to be added to an existing house.*

of wood construction. The two most common kinds of wood-framed construction now in use are *platform frame* and *plank and beam*.

Platform frame construction is a very economical, strong, and simple framing method. It provides a flat surface at each floor level on which to work. The subfloor extends to the outer edge of the building and provides a platform on which the exterior walls and interior partitions can be erected. Fig. 25-4. The joists, headers, and subfloors of each story form an independent unit which rests on the sills or top plates of the story below. Platform construction is the framing technique most often followed in one-story homes in most areas of the country. It is the kind most commonly used in prefabricated homes. Many homes are being built with a *trussed roof rafter.* Fig. 25-5 (P. 136).This allows the architect to design the interior of the house without a load-bearing wall.

The *plank and beam* method of construction of floors and roofs is particularly good for the modern designs of one-story homes. With this kind of construction, large glass areas and open space planning and natural finish of materials can be featured. The plank and beam method of framing uses beams that are spaced about 8 feet apart. Fig. 25-6.

DRAWINGS FOR A HOME

The views of a house are shown in *general* and *detail* drawings. General drawings include the plans and elevations, while detail drawings are made up of sectionals or sections and detail views. The drawings are made to some scale to show proportions. All information as to size must be shown by figured dimensions. The selection of a scale is determined by the size of the house as it is related to the paper size. The drawing must also be clear and easy to read. Scales commonly used are as follows:

General drawings use a scale of $1/4'' = 1'0''$. Less frequently a scale of $1/8'' = 1'0''$ is used. Detail drawings are prepared to scales of $3/8'' = 1'0''$, $1/2'' = 1'0''$, $3/4'' = 1'0''$ or $1 1/2'' = 1'0''$.

A complete set of working drawings consists of the following:

Presentation Drawing, or Pictorial Rendering. These are perspective drawings of a house showing how it will look when completed. These drawings are so lifelike that they appear to be a photograph of the house after it is built. Fig. 25-7 (P. 138).

Plans. A plan view corresponds to a top view. Several types are included:

Site or Plot Plan. This plan shows the outline of the lot and the location of the building on it. On more complete site plans, the contours, boundaries, existing roads, utilities, and other physical details such as trees are shown.

Foundation or Basement Plan. This plan is the top view of the footings or foundation walls showing the exact size and location of foundations. It may also include the major utilities such as the location of the furnace,

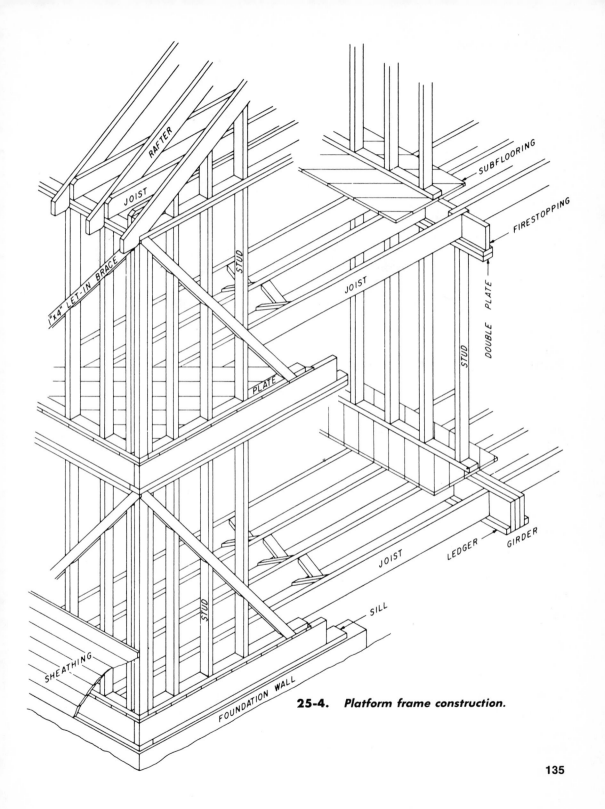

25-4. *Platform frame construction.*

Labels on figure: RAFTER, JOIST, 1"x4" LET-IN BRACE, STUD, SUBFLOORING, FIRESTOPPING, DOUBLE PLATE, JOIST, PLATE, STUD, JOIST, LEDGER, GIRDER, STUD, SILL, SHEATHING, FOUNDATION WALL

135

25-5. *A trussed roof rafter. Often the parts are fastened together with a plywood or metal gusset or plate. The trussed roof rafter makes it possible to have an open plan without interior walls to support the traditional rafter.*

floor drains, and other items that appear in the basement. Fig 25-8.

Building or Floor Plans. These are cross-section views of the house. The horizontal cutting plane cuts the building in such a way as to show all door and window openings. The floor plan shows the outside shape of the building, the arrangement, size and shape of rooms, the types of materials, the thickness of walls and partitions, and the type, size, and location of doors and windows. Since it is drawn to a very small scale, symbols are used to indicate fixtures and ma-

terials. Fig. 25-9 (P. 140). The plan may include other information, such as the electrical wiring and plumbing.

Framing Plans. These plans show the size, number, and location of structural members that make up the framework of the house. Separate framing plans are usually shown for the floor, roof, ceiling, and walls. The framing plans also show the sizes and spacing of the structural members. Fig. 25-10.

Elevations. Elevations are external views of the house made from the front, rear, right,' and left sides. Fig.

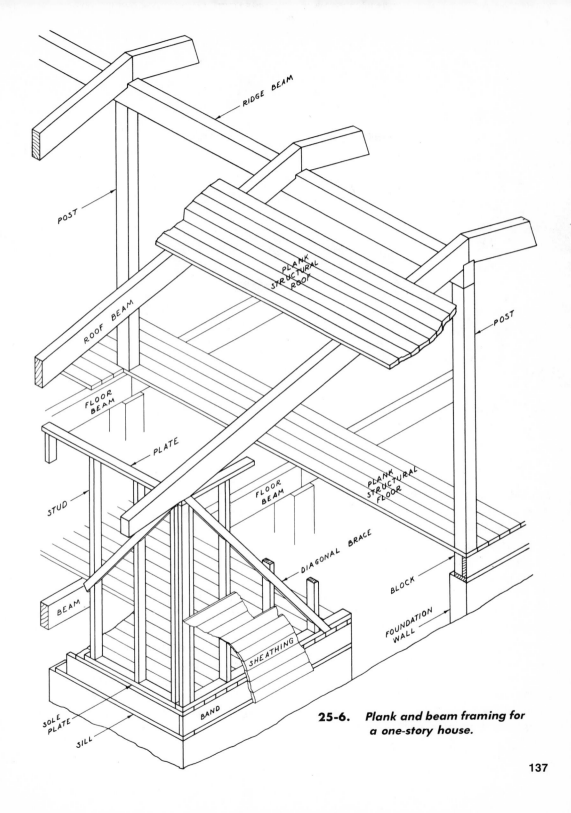

25-6. *Plank and beam framing for a one-story house.*

RIDGE BEAM

POST

POST

PLANK STRUCTURAL ROOF

ROOF BEAM

FLOOR BEAM

PLATE

PLANK STRUCTURAL FLOOR

STUD

FLOOR BEAM

DIAGONAL BRACE

BLOCK

FOUNDATION WALL

BEAM

SHEATHING

SOLE PLATE

SILL

BAND

25-7. *A presentation drawing, or pictorial rendering, of a home. Notice that it looks much like a photograph of the completed home.*

25-11 (P. 142). It is a picture-like view of the building that shows exterior materials, the height and width of doors, windows, and other items.

Sectional Views. Sectional views or sections show important information on building details. Fig. 25-12. They show how a house looks when cut vertically by a cutting plane. Sectional views are like elevations in that they show vertical projections. They are usually drawn to a larger scale than the elevations for clarity. *Typical sections* show a cross section of a wall while *detail sections* show the cross section of a certain part of the house, such as a cornice section.

Details. Details are larger scale drawings that show specific parts of the home. They may be detail drawings showing the construction of the kitchen cabinets. Other details may show various construction features.

Symbols for House Plans. Before you can read house plans, you must know the common architectural symbols. Symbols are very simplified drawings of the things they represent. Figs. 25-13 and 25-14 show the common symbols for doors and windows, building materials, and plumbing. In Fig. 25-15 (P. 146), a list of the common electrical symbols for home wiring is given.

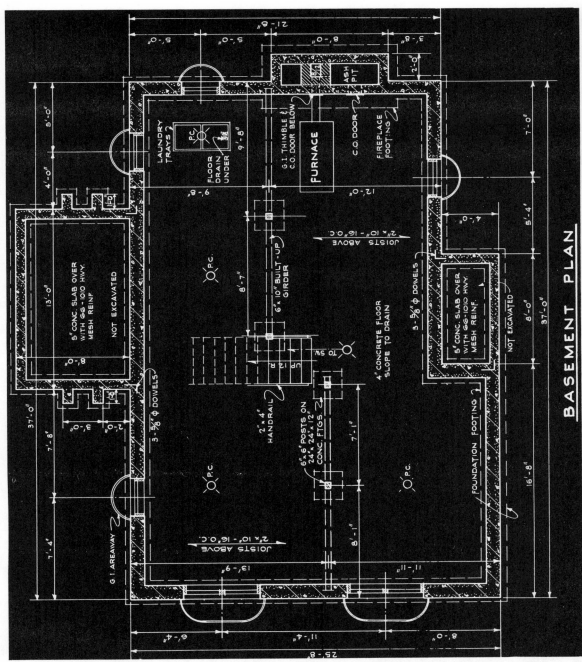

25-8. *This is the basement plan or foundation of a simple home. The illustrations that follow are for the same house.*

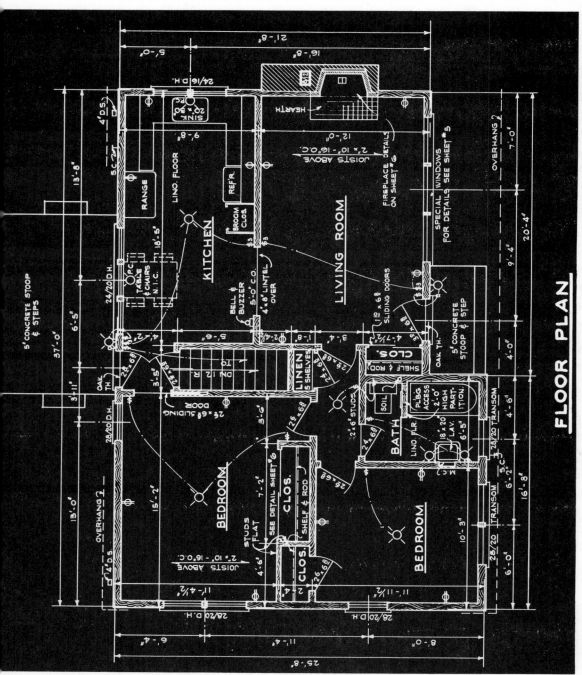

FLOOR PLAN

25-9. *This shows some of the standards for drawing a plan view of a home.*

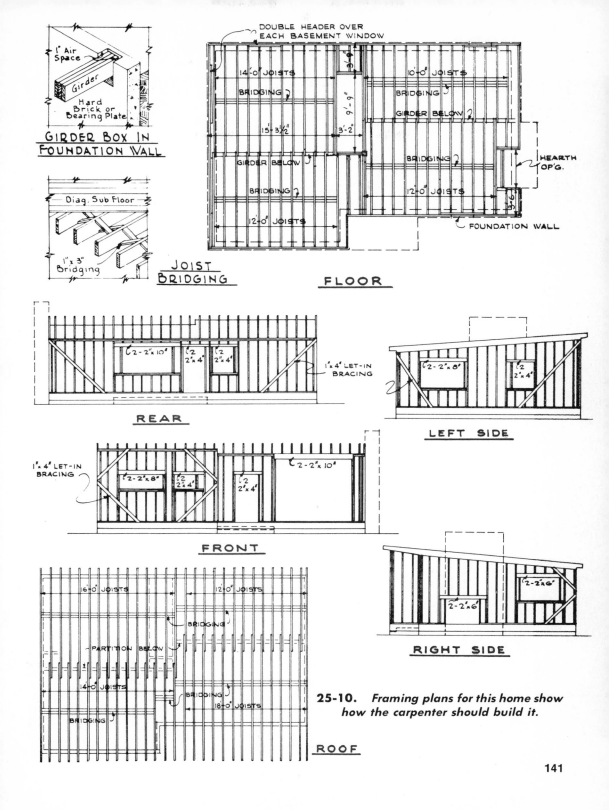

GIRDER BOX IN
FOUNDATION WALL

1" Air Space

Girder

Hard Brick or Bearing Plate

JOIST BRIDGING

Diag. Sub Floor

1" x 3" Bridging

FLOOR

DOUBLE HEADER OVER EACH BASEMENT WINDOW

14'-0" JOISTS

BRIDGING

15'-3½"

GIRDER BELOW

BRIDGING

12'-0" JOISTS

10'-0" JOISTS

BRIDGING

GIRDER BELOW

BRIDGING

12'-0" JOISTS

HEARTH OP'G.

FOUNDATION WALL

9'-9"

3'-2"

REAR

2-2"x10"

2 2"x4"

2 2"x4"

1"x 4" LET-IN BRACING

LEFT SIDE

2-2"x8"

2 2"x4"

FRONT

1"x 4" LET-IN BRACING

2-2"x8"

2 2"x4"

2 2"x4"

2-2"x10"

ROOF

16'-0" JOISTS

12'-0" JOISTS

BRIDGING

PARTITION BELOW

14'-0" JOISTS

BRIDGING

18'-0" JOISTS

BRIDGING

RIGHT SIDE

2-2"x6"

2-2"x6"

25-10. *Framing plans for this home show how the carpenter should build it.*

141

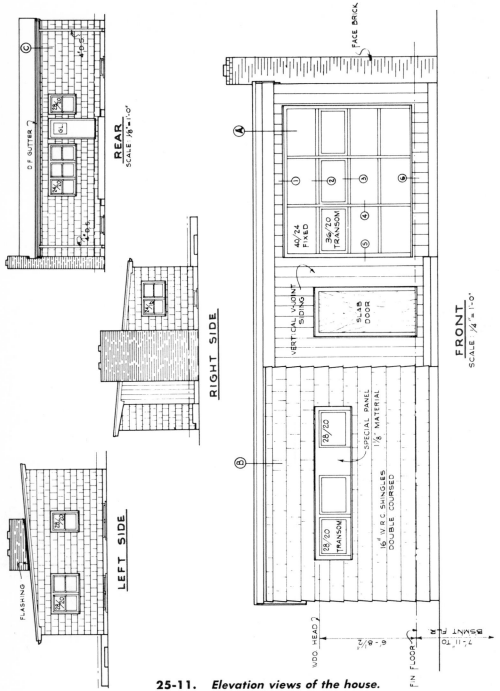

25-11. *Elevation views of the house.*

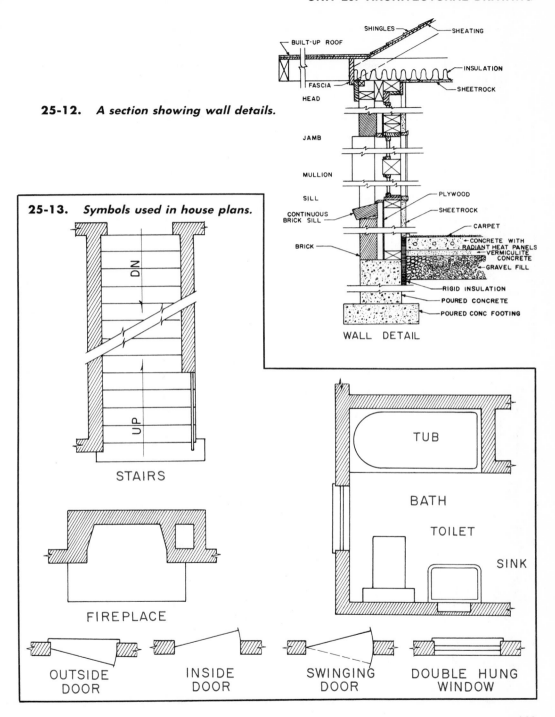

25-12. *A section showing wall details.*

25-13. *Symbols used in house plans.*

SHINGLES
SHEATING
BUILT-UP ROOF
INSULATION
FASCIA
SHEETROCK
HEAD
JAMB
MULLION
SILL
PLYWOOD
CONTINUOUS BRICK SILL
SHEETROCK
CARPET
BRICK
CONCRETE WITH RADIANT HEAT PANELS
VERMICULITE CONCRETE
GRAVEL FILL
RIGID INSULATION
POURED CONCRETE
POURED CONC FOOTING

WALL DETAIL

DN

UP

STAIRS

FIREPLACE

TUB

BATH

TOILET

SINK

OUTSIDE DOOR

INSIDE DOOR

SWINGING DOOR

DOUBLE HUNG WINDOW

EARTH ETC.
EARTH · ROCK · CINDER FILL · *SAND

INSULATION: LOOSE FILL OR BATTS · BOARDS, QUILTS · SOLID : CORK MAGNESIA

CONCRETE CEMENT
STONE · CINDER · CEMENT · CONCRETE CEMENT ELEVATION · BLOCK · PLANK · TERRAZZO

METALS
*STEEL, IRON · *CAST IRON · *BRASS, BRONZE · ALUMINUM · SHEET METAL, ALL METAL, SMALL SCALE · SHEET METAL ELEVATION · STRUCTURAL STEEL · REINFORCING BARS

BRICK
*COMMON · FACE · FACE BRICK ON COMMON · FIRE BRICK ON COMMON · ELEVATION · SPANDREL WALL · CORK INSULATION WITH METAL FACES

STRUCTURAL CLAY TILE
SMALL SCALE · LARGE SCALE · FLOOR UNITS · SMALL SCALE FACING · ELEVATION · LARGE SCALE TILE · ELEVATION

ARCHITECTURAL TERRA COTTA
VENEER · HOLLOW · SMALL SCALE PARTITION · ELEVATION BLOCK · SMALL SCALE FACING · SMALL SCALE

STONE
CUT STONE · RUBBLE · CAST STONE CONCRETE · MARBLE · SLATE BLUESTONE SOAPSTONE · ASHLAR · LARGE SCALE · ELEVATION · *RUBBLE · SQUARED STONE · ELEVATIONS

WOOD
*FINISH · ROUGH · SHINGLES SIDING ELEVATION · STUD WALL AND PARTITION · WOOD FINISH ON STUDS · SMALL SCALE · LARGE SCALE PLYWOOD · BOARD FLOORING

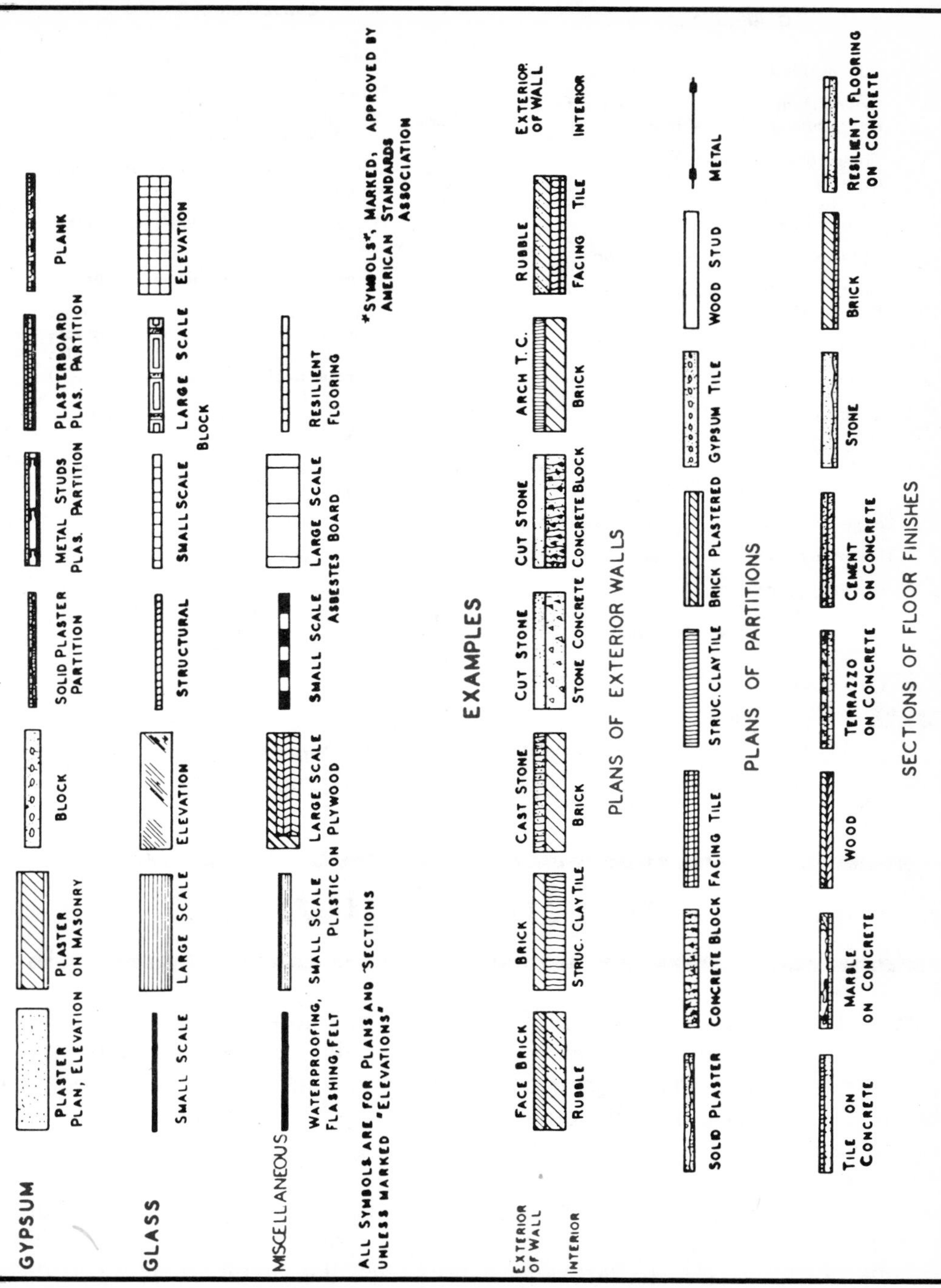

25-14. ***Building material symbols.***

General Outlets

○ Lighting Outlet

⌖ Ceiling Lighting Outlet for recessed fixture (Outline shows shape of fixture.)

⌀ Continuous Wireway for Fluorescent Lighting on ceiling, in coves, cornices, etc. (Extend rectangle to show length of installation.)

Ⓛ Lighting Outlet with Lamp Holder

Ⓛ₊PS Lighting Outlet with Lamp Holder and Pull Switch

Ⓕ Fan Outlet

Ⓙ Junction Box

Ⓓ Drop-Cord Equipped Outlet

Ⓒ Clock Outlet

Switch Outlets

S Single-Pole Switch

S₃ Three-Way Switch

S₄ Four-Way Switch

Miscellaneous

▨ Service Panel

▬ Distribution Panel

– – – – Switch Leg Indication. Connects outlets with control points.

Convenience Outlets

 Duplex Convenience Outlet

 Triplex Convenience Outlet (Substitute other numbers for other variations in number of plug positions.)

Duplex Convenience Outlet — Split Wired

 GR Duplex Convenience Outlet for Grounding-Type Plugs

 WP Weatherproof Convenience Outlet

 X″ Multi-Outlet Assembly (Extend arrows to limits of installation. Use appropriate symbol to indicate type of outlet. Also indicate spacing of outlets as X inches.)

 S Combination Switch and Convenience Outlet

 R Combination Radio and Convenience Outlet

⊙ Floor Outlet

R Range Outlet

 DW Special-Purpose Outlet. Use subscript letters to indicate function. DW-Dishwasher, CD-Clothes Dryer, etc.

25-15. *Partial list of electrical symbols for home wiring.*

Unit 26. Map Drawings

A map is a one-view drawing of some part of the world's surface. Have you ever taken an imaginary trip by looking at a map? It can tell you a great deal about the world in which you live.

Maps are of various kinds. A map may be made of the same area for many different purposes. A *highway* map of your state will show roads and cities, while a *conservation map* might show lakes, forests, streams, and fishing and hunting sites.

COMMON KINDS OF MAPS

Highway or Road Maps. A highway or road map shows the main highways, the distance between cit-

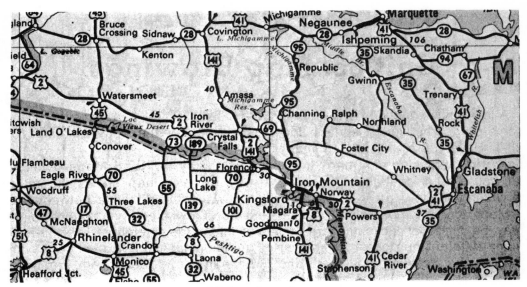

26-1. *A road map.*

ies and towns and, very often, points of interest to the tourist. Fig. 26-1. A guide on each map explains the symbols and how to read them. Fig. 26-2 (P. 148). Some highway maps are so complete they show state parks, museums, forests, airports, and many other things.

Maps always have a graphic scale to show the size of the map. You can use this scale to find the distances between cities and towns. It will also help you to estimate the distances you have traveled on a trip. Most maps show the distance between cities, with the number of miles lettered along the lines representing the highways and roads.

Airline Maps. An airline map shows the location of all the major cities served by aircraft. Fig. 26-3. The lines between the cities are drawn "as the crow flies," since airline maps show airline distances.

Railroad Maps. Since railroads usually follow natural terrain (such as rivers and valleys) between the cities they serve, the lines are not straight. Usually railroad maps make a route look straighter than it actually is.

Scenic, or Picture, Maps. Scenic, or picture, maps are actually picture drawings of an area. They are made for easy reading. Notice this scenic map of our national capital. Fig. 26-4. See how easy it is to find the major points of interest. This kind of map is very helpful to the tourist.

Maps for Special Purposes. Some maps are drawn to show the location of industrial plants, forests, mineral deposits, waterways, telephone cables, or any other special information.

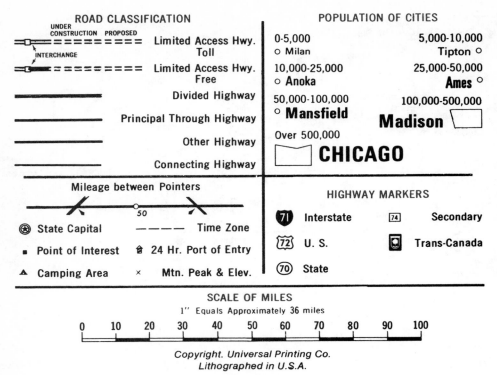

ROAD CLASSIFICATION

UNDER CONSTRUCTION   PROPOSED

INTERCHANGE

Limited Access Hwy. Toll

Limited Access Hwy. Free

Divided Highway

Principal Through Highway

Other Highway

Connecting Highway

Mileage between Pointers

50

⊛ State Capital   — — — — Time Zone

■ Point of Interest   ⚓ 24 Hr. Port of Entry

▲ Camping Area   × Mtn. Peak & Elev.

POPULATION OF CITIES

0-5,000
○ Milan

10,000-25,000
○ Anoka

50,000-100,000
○ **Mansfield**

Over 500,000
CHICAGO

5,000-10,000
Tipton ○

25,000-50,000
Ames ○

100,000-500,000
Madison

HIGHWAY MARKERS

71 Interstate   74 Secondary

72 U.S.   Trans-Canada

70 State

SCALE OF MILES
1″ Equals Approximately 36 miles

0   10   20   30   40   50   60   70   80   90   100

Copyright. Universal Printing Co.
Lithographed in U.S.A.

26-2. *This guide will help you read a road map.*

26-3. *An airline map.*

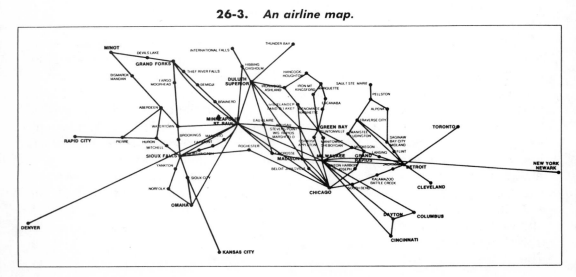

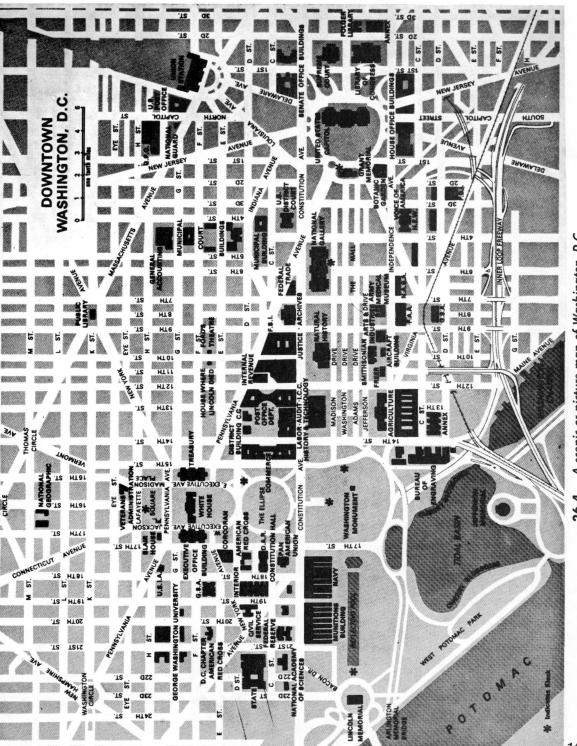

26-4. A scenic or picture map of Washington, D.C.

149

City Maps. City maps are drawn to show the location of streets, utilities such as water mains or sewer lines, sizes of property, and points of interest.

Plat Maps. When a person purchases a piece of city property, he or she secures an abstract of title to the land. In that title will be a map of the subdivision. This is called a *plat*. It shows the lot number, the exact size and description of each lot in the plat, the name and width of the streets, and other information of importance. Fig. 26-5.

Weather Maps. In your daily paper, on television, and in many magazines are shown or printed weather maps for the next day, week, or season. Fig. 26-6. These maps are simpler forms of maps made by the Weather Bureau.

Many modern weather maps are made from pictures taken by weather satellites. These satellites photograph cloud formations and transmit the signals to weather stations. These photographs are then printed and used to make maps which are sent all over the world. Fig. 26-7.

Topographic Maps. These are the most complete maps of areas that can be drawn. A topographic map shows everything contained in that particu-

26-5. *Section of a plat map of a new development.*

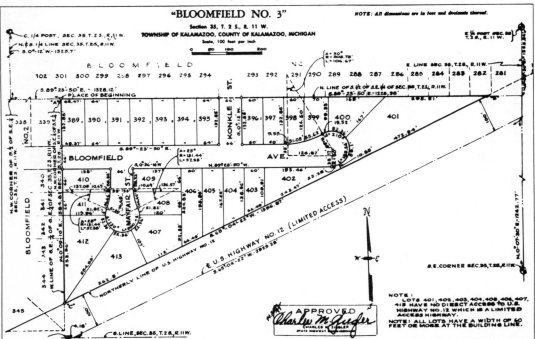

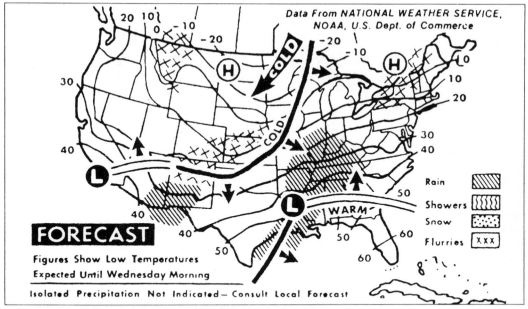

Data From NATIONAL WEATHER SERVICE,
NOAA, U.S. Dept. of Commerce

FORECAST

Figures Show Low Temperatures
Expected Until Wednesday Morning

Rain
Showers
Snow
Flurries

Isolated Precipitation Not Indicated — Consult Local Forecast

26-6.   A weather map of the United States.

26-7.   A meteorologist making weather maps from the printed photographs.

26-8. *A contour map showing a sketch of the land.*

lar area, including such natural things as lakes, streams, forests, and hills. Roads, buildings, and bridges are shown also. There are symbols for each of these. Some of the symbols are in color; so the map may be printed in various colors. Since maps are one-view drawings, they do not show elevations (height). To show hills or valleys, *contour lines* are drawn on the map. The closer together these lines are, the steeper is the slope or depression. These lines are numbered to show the height or elevation in feet in relation to some fixed elevation such as sea or lake level. Fig. 26-8. Maps of this type are made by civil engineers. They survey the land and make careful measurements and field notes. This information is transferred to a finished map drawing. Most of the maps used in everyday life are simpler forms of topographic maps.

Unit 27. Graphs and Charts

Graphs make facts and figures convenient to read, simpler to compare, and easier to understand. They add interest to any book or magazine by using pictures along with words and figures. There are four common kinds of graphs: *line and curve, bar, pictorial,* and *circle,* or pie.

LINE AND CURVE GRAPH

The line and curve graph is used to show what has happened or what might happen. For example, in Fig. 27-1 you see a line graph showing the number of drafters at work.

Proceed as follows to make a simple line and curve graph:

1. Select squared or cross-section paper. If the graph is to be made on plain paper, draw a grid (light lines that form equal-sized rectangles).

2. Draw a vertical line near the left (or right) edge of the paper. This line is called the *ordinate,* or Y axis. Draw a horizontal line near the bottom of the page. This is called the *abscissa,* or X axis. The place where the two lines join at the zero point is the *origin.*

3. Decide on what information is to be shown. Information that is made into a line and curve graph must contain two elements. One is constant such as years, months, number of games, etc. This is always placed along the horizontal line, or abscissa. The other information, such as the number or percentage of items, varies. This is placed along the vertical line, or ordinate.

4. Decide on the scale for the graph. The items that are constant must be in equal units. For example, in Fig. 27-1, each time period is ten years long. These units have to be placed an equal distance apart. The items that vary will determine the scale along the vertical line. Divide this space into equal units also. In Fig. 27-1, each space represents 25,000 drafters. Make the top unit larger than the largest amount to be shown on the graph.

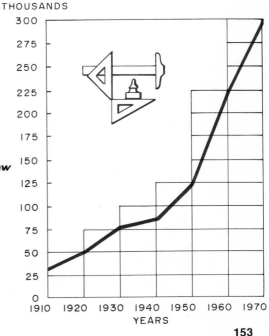

27-1. *A typical line graph used to show growth in the number of drafters.*

THOUSANDS

YEARS

5. Letter in the numbers along the horizontal and vertical lines. Be sure to show what the numbers represent.

6. Plot (locate) the points to make the graph line. For example, in 1910 there were 35,000 drafters. On a graph like Fig. 27-1, you would place a point on the 1910 line at 35. Plot other points the same way.

7. Draw a heavy line to connect these points.

8. Add the title and source of information. Make the title brief and easy to read.

9. Points to remember:

a. Make sure that the line or curve stands out in contrast to the background of the grid.

b. Keep the graph as simple as possible.

c. If there is more than one line, label each one. If possible, make the lines of different quality or kind.

d. Keep in mind the person who is going to read the graph.

BAR GRAPH

The bar graph is best for comparing such things as quantities, values, or percentages. The bars can be placed either vertically or horizontally. Fig. 27-2. If there are many items, draw the bars horizontally with the longest bar at the top. To make a simple bar graph such as the one in Fig. 27-2, proceed as follows:

1. Determine if it is to be a vertical or a horizontal bar graph.

2. Use cross-section paper or draw a series of horizontal or vertical lines. If the graph is on 8½" × 11" paper, make each line 1" away from the next. Letter each horizontal line with the units (in this case, 100). Always make sure there is one line beyond the largest bar.

3. Draw the bar a convenient width. Leave enough space between the bars. Fill in the bars to make them look solid.

4. Place a label beside each bar.

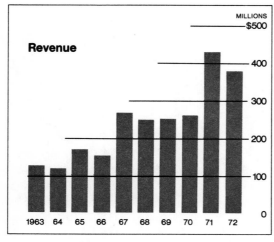

27-2. *A vertical bar graph.*

5. Add the title and source.

Sometimes double or triple bars are used to compare several items. Make sure that you show clearly what each bar means by cross-hatching each one in a different way. Always add a legend or code to identify each kind of bar. Bar graphs are made more interesting by adding a picture to illustrate what each bar represents.

CIRCLE, PIE, OR SECTOR GRAPHS

This kind of graph is very good for comparing information that totals 100 percent. Fig. 27-3. The circle equals 360 degrees. Therefore, each percent equals 3.6 degrees. A quarter of the circle is 25 percent. Suppose you wish to make a circle graph with the information on where our energy comes from: oil, 43%; natural gas, 32%; coal, 20%; hydroelectricity, 4%; and nuclear power, 1%. First draw a circle of the desired size. Since the oil figure is 43 percent, it would equal 154.8 degrees (43 × 3.6). Lay this angle off with the protractor and draw a line from the circumference to the center. Do this for each item of expenditure. Letter in each section of the pie, telling what each section represents and the percentage. Add the title. Patterns add to the appearance.

PICTORIAL GRAPH

The pictorial graph is a form of bar graph. Instead of using bars of different lengths, pictures or symbols are used. This makes the graph much more interesting to the reader. Fig.

FROM WHERE DOES OUR ENERGY COME ?

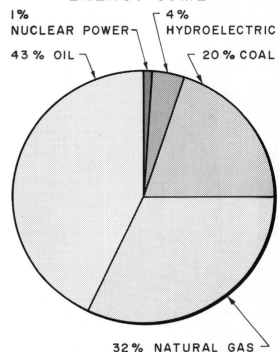

1% NUCLEAR POWER¬   ┌4% HYDROELECTRIC

43% OIL ¬   ┌20% COAL

32% NATURAL GAS ┘

27-3. *A circle, or pie, graph showing energy sources.*

27-4 (P. 156). The symbols should clearly represent the items.

CHARTS

Charts are a method of showing how things or people are related. The most common are organization and flow charts. The organization chart is used to show how people in any organization are related. In the school lab, for instance, there will be an organization chart showing how the shop is to be cared for. Fig. 27-5. The chart shows the position of each person

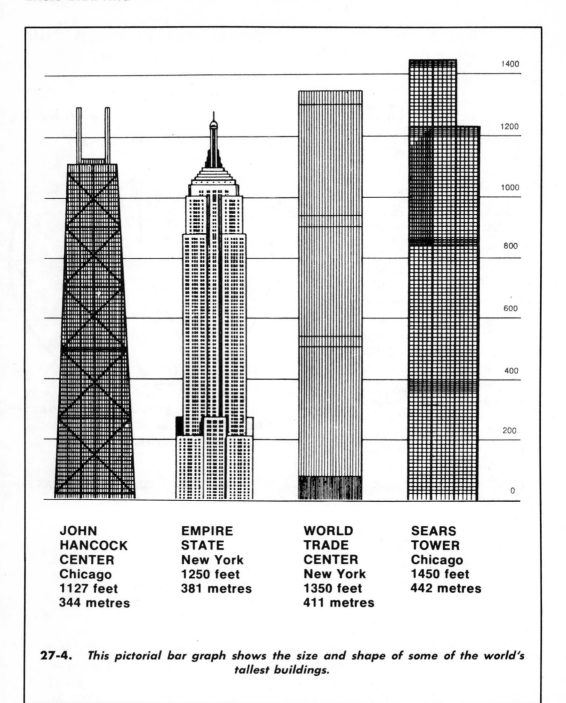

JOHN
HANCOCK
CENTER
Chicago
1127 feet
344 metres

EMPIRE
STATE
New York
1250 feet
381 metres

WORLD
TRADE
CENTER
New York
1350 feet
411 metres

SEARS
TOWER
Chicago
1450 feet
442 metres

27-4. *This pictorial bar graph shows the size and shape of some of the world's tallest buildings.*

and to whom that person is responsible. The flow chart shows how things are made, manufactured, and/or distributed. In Fig. 27-6, you see a flow chart showing how electricity is generated and distributed.

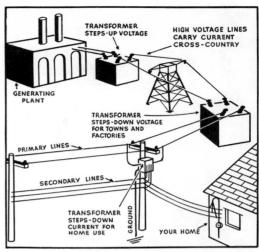

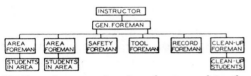

27-5. An organization chart used in the school lab.

27-6. A flow chart.

Unit 28. How Prints Are Made

Blueprints, or prints, are exact copies of mechanical drawings. You've heard of people getting a set of blueprints for the new house they are planning to build. These are copies of the original drawings made by the architect. They are called blueprints because the paper has a blue background with white lines. Most *copies of drawings* are called blueprints though they are not always blue.

HOW PRINTS ARE MADE

In manufacturing, building, and construction it would not be possible or desirable to use the original drawings. They would become soiled and worn out. Then, too, many workers have to handle the drawings at the same time; so several sets have to be made. In general, the first step in making a blueprint is to make a *tracing*.

28-1. *A blueprint machine.*

A thin sheet of transparent tracing paper or cloth is placed over the original drawing. The drawing is traced on this paper with pencil or ink. This tracing is then used in the same way a negative is used for making photographic snapshots. That is, the tracing is placed over some chemically treated paper and exposed to light. The treated paper is then developed to show the lines of the drawing.

BLUEPRINT MACHINE

Blueprint machines make prints quickly and easily. Fig. 28-1. There are many different sizes. On small ones the blueprint paper is cut to size and fed into the machine one sheet at a time. On large machines the process is a continuous one with the paper and tracing starting in at one end and the dry print coming out the other.

In blueprint machines the tracing is placed over the sensitized blueprint paper. Together they are fed into the front of the machine where they go under strong arc lights. The original yellow paper turns a greyish blue. The tracing is removed and the print washed in clear water. The paper turns blue with white lines. The print is then washed in potassium bichromate solution to darken it. It is washed again in water and then dried.

The disadvantage of blueprint printing is that the paper tends to shrink a little as it goes through the washing and drying. The chief advantage is that the finished print does not fade when exposed to sunlight. For this reason it is used very much in the building trades.

OZALID PROCESS (Dry Diazo)

This print has a white background with black, blue, or maroon lines, depending on the kind of sensitized paper used. A tracing is placed over the sensitized paper. This is fed through the printer, which exposes it to strong light. The tracing is then separated from the paper and the sensitized paper fed through a developer that exposes the paper to ammonia fumes. This produces a print that comes out of the machine perfectly dry. The print does not shrink at all and is smooth. Fig. 28-2. Because of the white background, changes can

DRY PROCESS
(OZALID)

SEMI-MOIST PROCESS
(BRUNING)

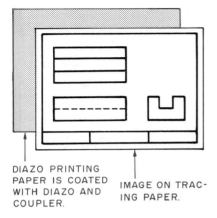

DIAZO PRINTING PAPER IS COATED WITH DIAZO AND COUPLER.

IMAGE ON TRAC- ING PAPER.

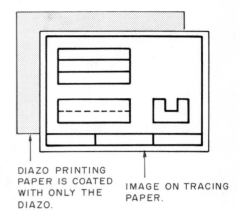

DIAZO PRINTING PAPER IS COATED WITH ONLY THE DIAZO.

IMAGE ON TRACING PAPER.

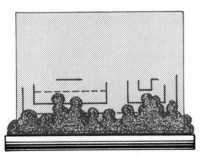

PRINT COMES IN CONTACT WITH AMMONIA FUMES.

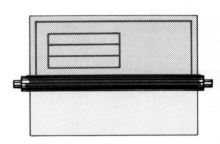

A CHEMICAL SOLUTION CONTAIN- ING THE COUPLER IS APPLIED TO THE PRINT BY A SERIES OF ROLLERS.

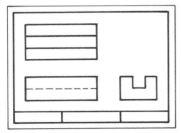

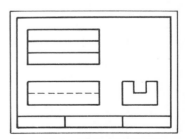

28-2. *A comparison chart of the ozalid and Bruning print-making processes.*

28-3. *Using the Bruning machine. The large tracing and sensitized paper are fed into the lower opening to expose the paper to ultraviolet light. The exposed paper is then fed through the developer.*

easily be made on the print with pencil or ink.

BRUNING COPYFLEX PROCESS (Moist Diazo)

This process is similar to the ozalid or dry diazo method of making prints. However, it uses a different kind of sensitized paper and a developing compound made by mixing developing salts in water. The machine does not have to be vented for fumes like an ozalid machine. The print is made by placing the tracing on the sensitized paper and exposing it to an ultraviolet light. The exposed sheet is then fed through the developing rolls. The liquid developer brings out the colored lines (usually brown or black, depending on the paper used) on a light background. Fig. 28-2. The finished print comes out slightly damp but dries almost immediately as it passes over a heater unit. Fig. 28-3.

MICROFILMING

Another print-making process used today is microfilming. This is a photographic process, just like taking pictures with a camera. The finished drawing (no tracing is needed)is fed into a machine. This machine reduces the size of the photographic image of the drawing and records it on negatives down to about $1/2''$ (12 mm) square. The drawings can then be stored for future use in very little space. Prints can be made by enlarging the small negative.

These negatives can also be used in a special reading machine. The drawings can then be studied, and if desired, a print of the drawing can be made.

OTHER DUPLICATING PROCESSES

There are many other methods of duplicating a drawing or tracing. A common way in many schools is to use a roller-type inking machine (mimeograph). Some school offices are equipped with a photographic duplicating machine or a dry duplicator that operates with heat-sensitive paper.

QUESTIONS AND TOPICS FOR DISCUSSION

UNIT 1

1. What are some reasons for learning to make and read drawings?

2. Why is drawing an important part of our industry?

3. Describe the following occupations: detailer, tool designer, architect, industrial designer, industrial teacher, and engineer.

4. What training and/or education is required for each of these occupations?

5. All drafters must attend a trade, vocational or technical school to learn their trade. True or False.

6. Most tool designers start as drafters or machinists. True or False.

UNIT 2

1. A pictorial drawing looks very much like a photograph. True or False.

2. The drawing most useful to the worker and builder is the perspective drawing. True or False.

UNIT 3

1. What equipment is needed for beginning drawing?

2. How are pencils graded? Which is harder, a 3H or an HB?

3. What is dual dimensioning?

UNIT 4

1. The T square and a triangle are used for drawing vertical lines. True or False.

2. The T square should be used with the head held against the top of the drawing board. True or False.

UNIT 5

1. One triangle used in drawing has two 45-degree angles and one 90-degree angle. True or False.

2. What is an acute angle? A right angle? An obtuse angle?

UNIT 6

1. The radius of a circle is one-half its diameter. True or False.

2. The diameter of a circle is the length of a straight line through the center. True or False.

3. A line that is tangent to a circle crosses through the circle. True or False.

UNIT 7

1. A scale of $1/2''$ equals $1'$ means that the drawing is made twice the size of the object. True or False.

2. What does it mean to make a drawing to scale?

UNIT 8

1. What tools are included in a set of instruments?

2. Name the two kinds of compasses.

3. What kind of pencil lead should be used in a compass?

4. What is the dividers needed for?

5. What is a civil engineer's scale used for?

6. What is a template?

7. To divide a line into equal parts, adjust the dividers by trial and error and space off the line. True or False.

8. Most drawings of rooms, buildings and house plans are made to one-fourth full size. True or False.

UNIT 9

1. Why do we need shop drawings or sketches?

2. What kind of paper is used to make the shop drawing or sketch?

3. What is an isometric shop drawing?

4. Shop sketches are complicated drawings that include a lot of detail. True or False.

UNIT 10

1. Are hard drawing pencils (3 or 4H) good for making freehand sketches?

2. When sketching a square, the first step is to sketch vertical and horizontal construction lines. True or False.

3. A straight line should be sketched in one stroke of the pencil. True or False.

4. All construction lines should be erased from a freehand sketch. True or False.

5. Tell how the following are drawn freehand: (a) a straight line, (b) a vertical or slant line, (c) a square or rectangle, (d) a triangle, and (e) a circle or arc.

UNIT 11

1. Why is it a good idea to draw a perspective sketch of a project before building it?

2. What is meant by technical illustrating?

UNIT 12

1. Why are some letters given more space than others? What is meant by open and closed letters?

UNIT 13

1. Give the meaning of these three kinds of dimensions: (a) over-all dimen-

sions, (b) position or location dimensions, (c) detail dimensions.

2. What are extension lines? Dimension lines?

3. Extension lines should start about $1/2''$ away from the outline of the object. True or False.

4. A leader to a hole should be drawn at an angle of 45 or 60 degrees to the horizontal. True or False.

5. The diameter of an arc should be dimensioned. True or False.

6. Always dimension the radius of circles and holes. True or False.

7. Notes on a drawing are usually lettered in $1/2''$ capitals. True or False.

UNIT 14

1. What is a one-view drawing? Can you name some examples of one-view drawings?

2. The lightest lines on the paper are the border lines. True or False.

3. Explain the information that goes into a title block or record strip.

UNIT 15

1. What is a working drawing?

2. What are the three main views used in a working drawing?

3. In a working drawing the height is shown on the front and right-side view. True or False.

4. In a working drawing the length is shown on the front and right-side view. True or False.

UNIT 16

1. An invisible or hidden line is a series of dashes about $1/8''$ long with white spaces between. True or False.

2. When is it necessary to use invisible or hidden lines?

UNIT 17

1. Tell what determines the number of views to use for a drawing.

2. Only two views are necessary to make a working drawing of a round hockey puck. True or False.

UNIT 18

1. What is a perspective drawing? Where is it best used?

UNIT 19

1. How is an isometric drawing made?

UNIT 20

1. What are the kinds of oblique drawings?

2. Where are cabinet drawings used a good deal?

3. In an oblique drawing one corner appears closer to you. True or False.

4. In a cabinet drawing the lines to form the top and sides are made twice the true length. True or False.

UNIT 21

1. What are assembly drawings? Detail drawings?

UNIT 22

1. What does a section view show?

2. When the front view is cut away it has what term applied to it?

3. What does the cutting plane line show?

4. What part has been cut away in a half section?

5. What is a removed or detail section?

UNIT 23

1. Auxiliary views are made as a part of a working drawing of irregularly shaped objects. True or False.

2. What kind of surface requires an auxiliary view?

3. What are some important points to remember in drawing auxiliary views?

4. In making an auxiliary view always draw the entire view and not just the slanted surface. True or False.

UNIT 24

1. To bisect an angle means to divide the angle into two equal parts. True or False.

2. A hexagon has nine equal sides and angles. True or False.

3. Laying out a round corner on a square table top would be drawing an arc tangent to lines at 90 degrees. True or False.

UNIT 25

1. There are about ten basic skilled trades in the building industry. True or False.

2. What is an architectural drawing?

3. What kind of paper is best for making a room arrangement or workshop layout?

4. How would you go about making a room arrangement or workshop layout?

5. Describe the following: floor plan, elevation, detail elevation, section, pictorial rendering.

UNIT 26

1. What, exactly, is a map?

2. Name the kinds of maps.

3. A plat map describes in detail a piece of city property. True or False.

4. The distance between Chicago and New York would be shown in the same way on both an airline map and a highway map. True or False.

UNIT 27

1. What sort of information is best shown on a line and curve graph?

2. Describe a bar graph. What is it used for?

3. What does the pictorial graph show?

4. What is a pie, or circle, graph? When is it used?

5. Describe charts and tell how they are used.

6. The vertical line near the right or left edge on a line graph is called the abscissa. True or False.

UNIT 28

1. What is a blueprint?

2. Why are blueprints necessary?

3. Describe the process of the blueprint machine.

4. What is the chief advantage and what is the chief disadvantage of blueprints?

5. Name other processes of reproducing prints.

6. A blueprint is an exact copy of a mechanical drawing. True or False.

7. In the ozalid process the color of the lines depends on the kind of print paper used. True or False.

8. A common way of duplicating drawings in the school lab is by mimeograph. True or False.

INDEX

A

Angles
   dimensioning, 82
   drawing, 37, 38
Angular perspective drawings,
   100–104
Architect's scale, 50, 51. *See also*
   Rules for measuring in drawing
Architectural drawings, 129–146
Architecture, 15
Arcs
   dimensioning, 82
   drawing, 42–44, 61
   sketching, 61
Arrowheads, 81
Assembly drawings, 111–115
Auxiliary views, 119–122

B

Bar Graph, 152, 154, 155
Blueprint (prints)
   Bruning copyflex process (moist
      diazo), 160
   machine, 158
   how made, 157
   microfilming, 160
Bow compass, 49
Bruning copyflex process (moist
   diazo), 160
Building details, sectional views,
   138
Building or floor plans, 136, 140

C

Cabinet
   drawings, 20, 21, 109–111
   sketching, 63, 65
Careers in drawing, 12–17
Cavalier drawings, 109

Circle graph, 155
Circles
   center, locating, 42, 43
   dimensioning, 82
   drawing, 43
   in isometric, drawing, 106
   sketching, 61
City maps, 150
Civil engineer's scale, 51, 52
Common conversions—customary to
   metric—metric to customary
   (table), 24
Compasses
   adjusting, 43
   kinds of, 42, 48
Construction
   geometric, 123–129
   kinds of, for a home, 132–134

D

Decimal and millimetre equivalents
   of parts of an inch (table), 25,
   26
Designer, 14, 16
Detail drawing, 111–115
Detailer, 13, 14
Diazo printmaking processes, 158–
   160
Dimensioning drawings, 78–81,
   83–85
Dimensions, or sizes, defined, 18,
   19
Dividers, 49, 50
Drafting machine, 54
Drawing bench and board, 32, 33
Drawing(s)
   adding notes to, 82
   angular perspective, 100–104
   architectural, 129–146

arcs, 42–44
arrowheads, 81
auxiliary view, 119–123
cabinet, 20, 21, 109–111
careers in, 12–17
cavalier, 109
circles, 42, 43
detail and assembly, 111–115
dimensioning, 78–81
dual dimensioning, 83–85
for a home, 134–145
horizontal lines, 32–36
illustrative and construction, 18
inclined (slanted) lines and angles, 36–41
instruments and equipment, 28–30, 32–35, 42, 43, 48–54
invisible or hidden lines, 96, 97
irregular curves, 42, 44, 45
isometric, 104–108
kinds of, 20, 21
maps, 146–152
multiview, 20
oblique, 109–111
one-view (layout), 86–89
paper, 34
pictorial, 20
scale, 45–48
sectional view, 115–119
sets (instruments), 48
simple drawing, how to start, 35, 36
teaching, 16
three-view, 94, 95
tools and materials, 28–30, 32–36
vertical lines, 32–36
visual communication, 17, 18
where you will use, 12
working, 20, 21, 89–95
working drawing with two views, 98, 99

Dual dimensioning, 83–85

E

Electrical symbols, 146
Elevations, 136, 142
Engineering, 16
Erasers, 34, 35

F

Foundation or basement plans, 134, 136, 139
Framing plans, 135–137, 141
Freehand sketching, 58, 62, 63. *See also* Sketching
Front and rear caliper hand brake parts list (table), 10

G

Gage-marking a line, 42
Graphs
and charts, 152–157
line and curve, 152–154
pictorial, 155, 156

H

Hidden lines, 96, 97
Highway or road maps, 146–148
Horizontal lines, 18, 19, 32–36

I

Illustrations
technical, definition of, 69, 70
types of, 70
Illustrative and construction drawings, 18
Illustrator, technical, 14, 15
Inclined (slanted) lines and angles, 36–41
Instruments and equipment used in drawing, 28–30, 32–35, 42, 43, 48–54

Invisible lines, 96, 97
Irregular curves, 42, 44, 45
Isometric drawing(s)
    angles in, 108
    definition of, 20, 21, 104
    dimensioning, 108
    exploded isometric, 106, 107
    making, 104–108
    shop drawing, 56, 57
    sketching, 63, 66

L

Lettering
    devices, 77
    kinds of, 71–73
    left-handed, 75
    numbers, 76
    practice, 73
    words and phrases, 75
Lines
    in drawing, 18
    for freehand sketching, 58, 59
    horizontal, 18, 19, 32–36
    inclined, and angles, 36, 41
    measuring accurately, 30, 31
    non-isometric, 105
    parallel, 38, 39, 41
    perpendicular, 39
    slanted or inclined, 18, 19
    vertical, 32–36

M

Maps
    airline, 147, 148
    highway or road, 146–148
    plat, 150
    railroad, 147
    scenic or picture, 147, 149
    topographic, 150, 152
    weather, 150, 151
Measurements, making, 22, 30, 31

Mechanical engineer's scale, 51
Metric scales (table), 53
Metric scales for metric drawing, 52, 53
Metric system, 22–24
Microfilming, 160
Mimeograph duplicating process, 160
Multiview drawing, 20

O

Oblique drawings, 109–111
One-view drawings, 86–89
Orthographic projection (working drawing), 20
Ozalid process (dry diazo), 158, 159

P

Paper, for drawing, 34
Parallel lines, drawing, 38, 39, 41
Parallel perspective drawings, 101
Pencil(s)
    for drawing, 28–30
    pointer and sharpener, 53
Perpendicular lines, drawing, 39
Perspective drawing(s)
    angular, 100–104
    definition of, 20
    kinds of, 100, 101
    parallel, 100, 101
    sketching, 67–70
Pictorial drawings, 20
Pie graph, 155
Plat maps, 150
Presentation drawing (pictorial rendering), 134, 138
Protractor, 39–41

R

Railroad maps, 147
Rule, reading, 24, 27, 28

Rules for measuring, 28. *See also* Architect's scale

S

Scale drawing, 45–48
Scales, common, for measuring, 48
Scenic or picture maps, 147, 149
Sectional view, drawing, 115–119
Sector graph, 155
Seven SI metric base units (table), 23
Shop sketch, making, 55–57
SI metric base units, 23
Site or plot plan, 134
Sketching
  cabinet, 63, 65
  circles and arcs, 61
  freehand, 58, 62, 63
  isometric, 63, 66
  squares and rectangles, 59, 60
  triangles, 61
Slanted or inclined lines, 18, 19, 36–38
Special-purpose maps, 147
Squares and rectangles, sketching, 59, 60
Straight lines, drawing, 30
Symbols

in drawing, 18, 19
electrical, 146
for house plans, 138, 143–146

T

Tape, 34
Templates, 54
Three-view drawings, 94, 95
Thumbtacks, 34
Tool designers, 15
Tools and materials for drawing, 28–30, 32–35, 42, 43, 48–54
Topographic maps, 150, 152
Triangles
  definition of, 36, 37
  drawing, 33, 34
  sketching, 61
T square, 33

V

Vertical lines, 18, 19, 32–36
Visual communication by drawings, 17, 18

W

Weather maps, 150, 151
Working drawings, 20, 21, 89–95, 98, 99